To my darling Theo
with all

IEE HISTORY OF TECHNOLOGY SERIES 16

Series Editor: Dr B. Bowers

CURIOSITY PERFECTLY SATISFYED

Faraday's travels in Europe 1813-1815

Other volumes in this series:

CURIOSITY PERFECTLY SATISFYED

Faraday's travels in Europe 1813~1815

Edited by

Brian Bowers and Lenore Symons

Peter Peregrinus Ltd. in association with The Science Museum, London

Published by: Peter Peregrinus Ltd., London, United Kingdom

© 1991: Peter Peregrinus Ltd.

Peter Peregrinus Ltd.,
Michael Faraday House,
Six Hills Way, Stevenage,
Herts. SG1 2AY, United Kingdom

British Library Cataloguing in Publication Data

ISBN 0 86341 234 3

A CIP catalogue record for this book
is available from the British Library

Printed by the Stamford Press Pte Ltd., Singapore

CONTENTS

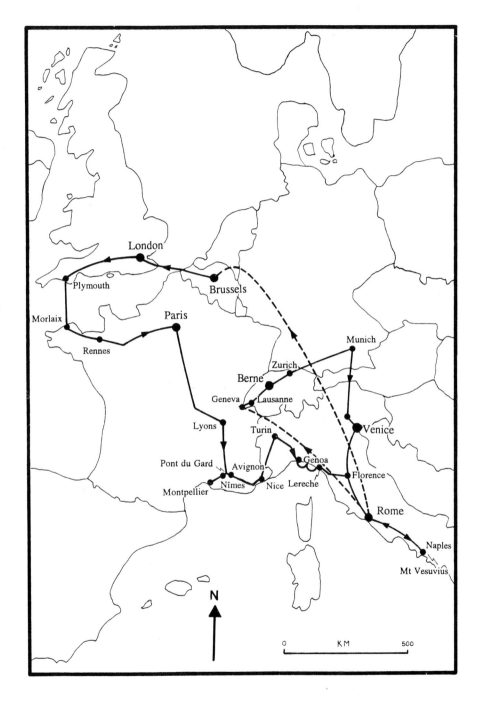

Route taken by Davy and Faraday

INTRODUCTION

Michael Faraday travelled through France, Italy and Switzerland with Sir Humphry Davy from 13 October 1813 to April 1815. This volume contains a transcript of Faraday's journal, with his own account of his travels, his observations, and the people he met. There are entries for almost every day up to 20 April 1814, when the manuscript breaks off in mid sentence. The manuscript is in a bound volume entitled 'Common Place Book Vol 2' in the Archives of the Institution of Electrical Engineers, to whom it was given in 1915 by David James Blaikley, the brother-in-law of Jane Barnard, Faraday's niece to whom he left his notebooks and correspondence.

The text is a fair copy in Faraday's hand, apparently from an original written while in Europe. Most of the entries read like contemporary notes. There is no evidence of later editing. At several points he left a gap, intending to fill some detail in later.

The volume measures 24.5 by 19cm, and was presumably bound by Faraday himself, since he had trained as a bookbinder. The paper is watermarked 1815. The narrative is interrupted by a diary of his visit to Wales in 1819. That Welsh diary was edited by the late Dafydd Tomos and published in 1972 in his *Michael Faraday in Wales*. The European diary is published in full here for the first time. Later in the volume are Geological Notes written in the Isle of Wight in July 1824.[a]

We have also included in this volume, at the appropriate places, several letters written by Faraday while in Europe.[b] These both supplement the account given in the diary and continue the story after the diary manuscript ends. Indeed, a possible interpretation of passages in the letters is that, having got behind with his diary, Faraday envisaged the letters as taking its place.[c] Most of these letters are to his friend

---

a   The manuscript pages are numbered from 1 to 522. This journal occupies pages 1 to 46 and 207 to 341. The Welsh diary occupies pages 49 to 204, and the Isle of Wight notes 393 to 398. Presumably Faraday intended to complete transcribing his European journal in pages 342 to 392. Pages after 398 are blank.

b   Some of the original letters are in the Archives of the Institution of Electrical Engineers, Warner Papers. Where the letters have previously been published in L. Pearce Williams, **Selected Correspondence of Michael Faraday,** 1967, this is noted and cited as **LPW**. In some cases we have quoted letters from Henry Bence Jones, **Life and Letters of Faraday,** 1870, cited hereafter as **BJ**. Two editions were published in 1870. We used the first; the material is also in the second edition but the pagination differs. Bence Jones had access to some manuscripts which are no longer extant. He omitted some passages, indicated by . . .

c   In Faraday's letter to Benjamin Abbott, commenced 1 May 1814, he says that, if the letter cannot be despatched soon, 'I shall keep it by me & add to it as to a journal'. In a later letter (6 September 1814) he comments 'my journal is much behind hand'.

Benjamin Abbott and to Benjamin's elder brother, Robert. Others are to Faraday's mother, his sisters Elizabeth and Margaret, and his friend, T. Huxtable.

Additional material comes from Henry Bence Jones' *Life and Letters of Faraday*, published in 1870. He quotes passages from Faraday which could have been taken from the manuscript we now have (but if so, he did not always copy accurately). He also quotes passages which are of a later date than the last date in the surviving manuscript. This suggests that he had access to the original journal, and not just the fair copy which now survives. Bence Jones, however, mixed extracts from the journal and extracts from letters in order to make a consecutive narrative. It could be that the 'Bence Jones' material which comes neither from the journal as we have it, nor from extant letters, was taken from other letters which do not survive. Whatever the origin of this material, it enables us to follow Faraday for the remainder of his travels.

Faraday did not intend the diary for publication. His purpose, according to a note he made near the end, was 'to recall to my mind at some future time the things I see now and the most effectual way to do that will be I conceive to write down be they good or bad or however imperfect my present impressions'.

Faraday said he had never previously travelled further than three miles from London[d], but he had boundless curiosity and proved to be an observant traveller. His descriptions of the journey, the scenery and the manners and customs of the people make an interesting narrative in themselves. For the young man from London - he was twenty-two - the 'mountains' of Devon were a revelation and crossing the English Channel from Plymouth to Morlaix was to enter a new world.

Faraday had completed his apprenticeship as a bookbinder, but reading scientific books that came in for binding had given him a taste for science. He obtained a post as laboratory assistant at the Royal Institution, in London. The Institution had been founded in 1799 by an American, Benjamin Thompson, who had been given the title Count Rumford by the King of Bavaria. The purpose of the Institution was to encourage the application of science to 'the common purposes of life'. Rumford himself had applied scientific principles to the design of fireplaces, and Faraday was very critical of smoky French fireplaces.

Sir Humphry Davy was Professor of Chemistry at the Royal Institution; he was making important discoveries in chemistry and also drawing large crowds to lectures in which he expounded the latest scientific advances. He had made occasional trips around the British Isles collecting geological specimens and taking Faraday's predecessor, William Payne, to assist. In 1813 he resigned his position in order to make a much more extensive tour, and he invited Faraday to go with him. It is a tribute to him and his work that, having known him only a few months,

---

d   See Journal for 15 October 1813.

Davy wanted to take him on the journey. Davy had also intended to take his valet, La Fontaine, but a few days before their departure La Fontaine refused to go. Faraday was persuaded to take on extra duties on the understanding that Sir Humphry would engage a new valet in Paris, but in the event a suitable person could not be found. Lady Davy and her maid went too. Lady Davy is nowhere mentioned in the journal, though Faraday comments on her treatment of him in two of the letters.[e] While in Geneva the Davys and Faraday visited Dr Alexander Marcet and his wife Jane. Jane Marcet's *Conversations on Chemistry* was one of the books which first aroused Faraday's interest in science, and especially in electrochemistry. Roger de Candolle, a descendant of the botanist Augustin Pyramus de Candolle, relates an anecdote about a dinner given by the Marcets. As Mrs Marcet was about to lead her guests into the dining room, Lady Davy turned to Faraday, saying, 'Mr Faraday, you will now go and eat your meal in the kitchen.' The unfortunate Faraday vanished below stairs while the rest of the party seated themselves at table. At the end of dinner, when the ladies rose to leave the gentlemen, their host was heard to remark in a loud whisper, 'and now, my dear Sirs, let us go and join Mr Faraday in the kitchen.'[f]

Britain and France had been at war since 1793. The Peace of Amiens, signed in March 1802, had provided a brief respite until hostilities resumed in May 1803, and after that virtually all British subjects in France were prisoners of war or civilian detainees. However, despite the war, especially by 1813, there were some contacts between the two countries. Limited trade was allowed under licence and occasionally prisoners of war were exchanged.

When Davy and Faraday set out for France they left a Britain where the Prince Regent ruled and Lord Liverpool was Prime Minister. In Hampshire Jane Austen would soon begin writing *Emma*, one of her novels of contemporary life among the gentry. Like Faraday, Emma Woodhouse had never travelled far enough to see the sea. In France Napoleon still ruled, but his position had been severely weakened by the loss of his army during the retreat from Moscow at the end of 1812. In October 1813 he was defeated at the Battle of the Nations at Leipzig, but it was not until April 1814 that the success of the Allied coalition against him forced him to abdicate. He was exiled to the Mediterranean island of Elba from which he escaped to land in France on 1 March 1815. He was finally defeated at the Battle of Waterloo on 18 June 1815.

In addition to establishing government by Paris-appointed Prefects in the Departments of France and instituting the great administrative and legal code which bears his name, Napoleon had improved communications throughout France, building new canals, roads and ports.

---

e   Letters, Faraday to Benjamin Abbott, 25 January and 23 February 1815.
f   Quoted in Mavis Coulson, **Southward to Geneva: 200 Years of English Travellers**, Allan Sutton, Gloucester, 1988.

He also began a building programme in Paris. The new, arcaded, Rue de Rivoli was completed, triumphal arches were begun, and an addition to join the Louvre to the Tuileries was under construction. By 1814 there were 4,500 gas lamps lighting the streets of Paris. The Louvre Museum had been immeasurably enriched by works of art from all over Europe, the spoils of Napoleon's campaigns.

Under Napoleon the sciences had flourished. At the Jardin des Plantes a group of able men conducted research. Faraday noted that among them were M. E. Chevreul, R. J. Haüy, G. Cuvier and P. L. Dulong. Joseph Louis Gay-Lussac gave public lectures on chemistry and Davy and Faraday went at least once to hear him while they were in Paris.

French chemical industry was in advance of the British, especially in the production of alkali, mainly caustic soda used in the manufacture of soap and glass. The traditional source for alkali had been the ashes of certain plants, mainly seaweeds. Increasing demand, aggravated in the case of France by difficulty in importing materials during the war, led to a search for new sources. In 1785 the Académie des Sciences had offered a substantial prize for anyone who could solve the problem. Nicolas LeBlanc devised his soda process, for which he was granted a patent in 1789. The LeBlanc process involved heating together sodium sulphate, chalk (calcium carbonate) and coal (mainly carbon). The sodium sulphate was obtained by reacting common salt and sulphuric acid. At least one British soap manufacturer visited Paris during the brief period of peace in 1802 to study the industry. Davy and Faraday would have been equally eager to see the latest advances.

Davy's visit had been made possible by special permission from Napoleon. One of Davy's great chemical achievements had been the decomposition of the alkalis and the isolation for the first time of the metals potassium, sodium, calcium, barium, strontium and magnesium by using electricity to decompose their oxides. In Paris the Institut Impérial persuaded Napoleon that, as a patron of science, he ought to allow Davy to examine the geology of the extinct volcanoes in the Auvergne and the active ones in Naples, in the expectation that his analyses of the rocks would enhance the scientific understanding of volcanoes.[g] That objective was probably not fulfilled, but it is clear from Faraday's comments that they did study the geology in detail as they travelled.

Faraday was a keen observer and gives good descriptions which a modern geologist can appreciate. He does not himself interpret what he sees, but records any interpretations given by Davy. It was the middle of the period of much geological classification work. They took a

g   John Ayrton Paris, **The Life of Sir Humphry Davy**, Henry Colburn & Bentley, London, 1831, p267, gives volcanic investigations as the principal reason for the visit. John Davy (Sir Humphry's brother) in his **Memoirs of the Life of Sir Humphry Davy**, Longman, Rees, Orme, Brown, Green & Longman, London, 1836, p479, mentions, but does not emphasize, the volcanic studies.

particular interest in hot springs, as well as volcanoes, but do not seem to have related the two.

The visit attracted some criticism in the English press. *The Times* reported the party's arrival at Plymouth, and commented

> *We cannot help thinking, that while so large a portion of the Continent (Spain included) is, either through our bravery, or that of our Allies, open to the researches of science, Sir HUMPHREY [sic] might have spared himself the trouble of accepting any favour from the enemy of his country, by visiting France first. We should not be sorry, if BUONAPARTE sent him to keep company with the first victims of Corsican treachery at Verdun. Neither, we believe, would his Imperial Majesty be at all nice about it, if he thought the Professor worth keeping.*[h]

Davy's party sailed from Plymouth in the 'cartel' *Collingwood* on Sunday 17 October 1813 and reached Morlaix, in Brittany, early on the following Tuesday morning. Morlaix was the only port designated by France for communication under flag of truce. A 'cartel' was normally a ship used for exchanging prisoners of war, but since Faraday makes no mention of prisoners in the journal it seems unlikely that this ship carried any.

In Paris their most important chemical work was Davy's study of a new substance, iodine, which French chemists had isolated from seaweed. Davy found that it could not be broken down electrically and concluded that it must be an element, and similar to chlorine which he had already shown could not be decomposed. The elementary nature of chlorine was a matter of some controversy and not accepted by all chemists. The French chemist Antoine Laurent Lavoisier (1743-1794) had held that all acids contained oxygen. Hydrochloric acid (then called muriatic acid) must therefore contain oxygen and chlorine must be the oxide of an element, not yet isolated, called 'murium'.

After two months in Paris, Davy and Faraday travelled south to Montpellier where they stayed a month before crossing the Alpes Maritimes between Nice and Turin. Faraday described vividly crossing the snow-covered Col de Tende on foot, while the carriage and other members of the party were transported on sledges. They arrived in Turin on the last day of Carnival. In Genoa Faraday assisted Davy with the investigation of electric fish and attended an opera which he found tedious. From there the party sailed down the coast to Lerici in a small boat, spending a night on shore en route in bad weather. The next

---

h   **The Times**, 19 October 1813, p3, col4. See also **The Examiner**, Sunday 24 October 1813, pp673-675. (**The Times** refers to Portsmouth, rather than Plymouth, and the much longer article in **The Examiner** copies the error). Verdun was the principal depôt for British officer prisoners and upper and middle class civilian detainees.

extended stay was in Florence, where Faraday was happier than in any preceding city. Here Davy used the Grand Duke of Tuscany's 'great burning glass' to analyse diamond and also experimented with iodine. Faraday found 'an inexhaustible fund of entertainment and improvement' in the Natural History Museum where he saw Galileo's first telescope and eighteenth-century anatomical wax figures. After nearly a month in Florence they travelled to Rome where Faraday noted that 'now in the midst of things curious and interesting something arises every day which calls for attention and observations'. 'The relics of ancient Roman magnificence, the grandeur of the churches and their richness also' fascinated him.[i] He commented that 'every day presents sufficient to fill a book'.[j] Judging from the French influence on his spelling of Italian names, it is probable that Faraday used a French guidebook while exploring Rome.

Rome had reverted to papal rule in 1814, having been part of the French Empire. Here Davy and Faraday stayed until the summer while Davy conducted more experiments on carbon. From Rome they travelled to Naples to visit Vesuvius, which Faraday climbed twice, once in the day and once at night, when the evening meal was cooked by the heat of volcanic steam. By August they were in Geneva, then they travelled slowly through Switzerland and part of Germany to return to Italy. By 2 November 1814 they were back in Rome and stayed until the following spring. Davy had intended to travel further east from Italy, but curtailed the trip and returned quickly to London. The reason may have been that plague broke out in Malta, or it may have been because of the political situation after Napoleon's escape from Elba. They arrived back in London on 23 April 1815.[k]

Faraday found that 'the constant presence of Sir Humphry Davy was a mine inexhaustible of knowledge and improvement; and the various & free conversations of those countries through which I passed . . . continually afforded entertainment and instruction'.[l]

He had also made useful personal contacts. In Paris he met André-Marie Ampère, and the two had an extensive correspondence about electromagnetism during the 1820s. In Italy Count Alessandro Volta gave him a voltaic pile, which is still preserved in the Royal Institution. In Switzerland he met Gaspard de la Rive (1770-1834) and his son Auguste (1801-1873), and began a friendship which continued in correspondence and personal visits for the rest of his life.[m]

---

i   Faraday to his mother, 14 April 1814.
j   Faraday to Benjamin Abbott, 1 May 1814.
k   John Davy, op cit, p504. Faraday does not give the exact date of return, nor a clear reason, though reference to quarantine regulations suggests that that was a factor. See below his letter to his mother from Brussels, 16 April 1815.
l   Faraday to Robert Abbott, 16 August 1814.
m   Letters from Faraday to Ampère and to the de la Rives are in **LPW**. Letters from Ampère to Faraday are in L. du Launay, **Correspondance du Grand Ampère**, Paris, 1936.

For Faraday, seeking to establish himself as a scientist, the journey was the best possible education and preparation for his future career.

EDITORIAL POLICY

Our aim has been to present Faraday's text as accurately as possible. His handwriting is clear and there are few places in the journal where we were uncertain what he wrote. The manuscript letters, however, are badly faded and difficult to read. Where we were not sure of a word it is followed by a question mark in square brackets, thus [?]. Where Faraday left a space we have put a similar space thus [   ]. All curved brackets have been transcribed from the original text, whether Faraday's or Bence Jones'. We have corrected some errors, but only where we felt there was a slip of the pen which Faraday himself would have corrected had he noticed; occasionally we have supplied missing letters in square brackets. We are sometimes unable to distinguish between the lower case 's' and 'z' in Faraday's hand, though the capital letters are quite distinct. In copying from the manuscript we have supplied some full stops and commas. In copying from Bence Jones, however, we have omitted numerous commas. Faraday was sparing with his punctuation, though in some cases the ink may have faded. Bence Jones supplied commas liberally. Some long, complex sentences we have broken up with semicolons thus [;] but most of the long sentences are fairly easy to read. Place names have been transcribed as Faraday gave them, with notes added where necessary.

In Paris and Rome Faraday was fascinated by the architecture and monuments he saw and parts of the diary read like a guide-book. Since Faraday visited these cities, the functions and names of some buildings have changed, as has the identification of some classical remains. Where possible, we have tried to clarify these in the notes.

FURTHER READING

For a full-length biography of Faraday, see L. Pearce Williams, *Michael Faraday: a biography*, Chapman & Hall, London and New York, 1965.

For more recent, briefer, accounts see Brian Bowers, *Michael Faraday and the Modern World*, EPA Press, Wendens Ambo, 1991, and Geoffrey Cantor, David Gooding and Frank A. J. L. James, *Faraday*, Macmillan, Basingstoke, 1991.

Recent studies of aspects of Faraday's life and work will be found in David Gooding and Frank A. J. L. James (Eds), *Faraday Rediscovered - Essays on the Life and Work of Michael Faraday, 1791-1867*, Macmillan, Basingstoke, 1985

Henry Bence Jones, *The Life and Letters of Faraday*, 2 volumes, London, 1870. A second edition, slightly shortened, was published later the same year.

Biographies of Humphry Davy, especially those cited above, also shed light on the journey.

ACKNOWLEDGEMENTS

We are grateful to many people for information and comment, including: Christine Blondel, Faith Bowers, Keith Bowers, Paolo Brenni, Dick Fifield, Frank James, Michael Lynch, Helen Purves, Jean Robertson, John Symons, Rosemary Taylor, Michael Teague, and David Woodcock.

Brian Bowers   Lenore Symons
Science Museum   Institution of Electrical Engineers
London SW7   London WC2

Journal &c.

1813 Oct.   England. London.

Wednesday 13th This morning formed a
new era in my life. I have never before within my
recollection left London at a greater distance than twelve
miles and now I leave it perhaps for many years and
to visit spots between which and home whole realms will
intervene. 'Tis indeed a strange venture at this time to
trust ourselves in a foreign and hostile country where also so
little regard is had to protestations and honours that the slightest
suspicion would be sufficient to separate us for ever from England
and perhaps from life. But curiosity has frequently incurred
dangers as great as these and therefore why should I wonder
at it in the present instance. If we return safe the pleasures
of recollection will be highly enhanced by the dangers encountered

The first page of the original manuscript

JOURNAL &c

England, London

Wednesday 13th. This morning formed a new epoch in my life. I have never before within my recollection left London at a greater distance than twelve miles and now I leave it perhaps for many years and to visit spots between which and home whole realms will intervene. 'Tis indeed a strange venture at this time to trust ourselves in a foreign and hostile country where also so little regard is had to protestations and honour that the slightest suspicion would be sufficient to separate us for ever from England and perhaps from life. But curiosity has frequently incurred dangers as great as these and therefore why should I wonder at it in the present instance. If we return safe the pleasures of recollection will be highly enhanced by the dangers encountered and a never failing consolation is that whatever be the fate of our party variety a great source of amusement and pleasure must occur.

We left London about 11 o clk on this fine morning and I believe all the party bade an impressive mental adieu to the well known localities of Hyde park corner, the park, Kensington &c. The day was beautiful & the scenery new and fine but I cannot say I paid much attention to it. We sleep tonight at Amesbury?

Thursday 14th. We set off early this morning with cool weather and soon got on to Salisbury Plain. During our progress we saw at a distance the singular structure of Stone-henge but did not go to it, Plymouth being the point of attraction which had most force at this time. The numerous hillocks on the plain reminded me of the various accounts given of them but our passing view did not permit me to increase my stock of information on this point. We got on as fast as possible to Exeter at which place we arrived rather late and put up for the night. I have before me at this time the Cathedral but it is too dark to see it distinctly.

Friday 15th. Reached Plymouth this afternoon.[1] I was more taken by the scenery today than by anything else I have ever seen. It came upon me unexpectedly and caused a kind of revolution in my ideas respecting the nature of the earths surface. That such a revolution was necessary is I confess not much to my credit and yet I can assign to myself a very satisfactory reason in the habit of ideas induced by an acquaintance with no other green surface than that within 3 miles of London. - Devonshire however presented scenery very different to this. The mountainous nature of the country[2] continually put forward new forms & objects and the landscape changed before the eye more rapidly than the organ could observe it. This day gave me some ideas of the pleasures of travelling and have raised my expectations of future enjoyments to a very high point.

We entered Plymouth early in the afternoon and put up at the Commercial Inn. By the time that the dirt of Devonshire was removed the dinner was ready and soon after the meal was over I felt inclined to rest. Travelling I take it is fatiguing work but perhaps a little practice will enable one to bear it better.

Saturday 16th. The wind has been very high for several days and directly against a departure from this port. The view out to sea is very fine from the enormous swell of waters which comes rolling in from the Atlantic ocean. I went up to the Barracks the french prisons &c and ramble'd much about the town which is a close compact place and with a bustling appearance. There is very fine abrupt scenery about it and particularly towards the harbour.

Sunday 17th. This morning as the wind still continued to oppose us we went across the bay to Mount Edgecombe[3] but we had not been long in those fine grounds before we were hastily called away by the Captain of our Cartel[4] and directed to go on board for the wind was changed and now set in the right corner. On returning however to town much delay occurred with the Jewish money changers, who refused though they wished, to transact business before sunset.[5] Our captain endeavoured to cheat them of a little time by shutting the windows lighting candles and shewing them his advanced watch and it is believed that he would have prevailed as a jew was just going to take the bag out of his pocket when his wife came & to his sorrow told him the hour and

---

1   London to Amesbury and Amesbury to Exeter are both eighty-five miles. Exeter
        to Plymouth is forty-five miles. They travelled in their own carriage, hiring horses
        on the way.
2   Dartmoor.
3   Mount Edgecumbe, home of the Edgecumbe family, dates from the Tudor period and
        is surrounded by a park and gardens landscaped during the eighteenth century.
4   A 'cartel' was a ship permitted to ply between countries at war, normally for
        exchanging prisoners.
5   This was the ninth day of the Feast of Tabernacles.

as <u>she</u> knew that <u>he</u> then knew it he patiently and we impatiently waited until the sun was beneath the horizon. This delayed things very much and it was quite dark before we stepped into the boat which took us on board for the Cartel had moved from the quay and we thus lost the receeding view of Plymouth having nothing in exchange for it but a cold night and the lighthouse.

Monday 18th. - I last night had a fine opportunity of observing the luminous appearance of the sea and was amused by it for a long time. As the prow of the vessel met the waters it seemed to turn up a vast number of luminous bodies about the size of peas some however being larger than others. These appeared to roll onwards by the side of the vessel with the waters and sometimes traversed a distance of many yards before they disappeared. They were luminous at or beneath the surface of the water indifferently and the only effect produced by different depths was a diminution of the light by the quantity of intervening medium. These luminous spots were very numerous, the most so I think about half an hour after midnight. Their light was very bright and clear. The swell on the sea was very considerable all night though gradually decreasing. - I remained on deck and escaped all sea sickness. As day came on and the light increased we looked about us but saw nothing in the scene except sky and immense waves striding one after the other at a considerable distance. These as they came to us lifted up our small vessel and gave us when on their summits a very extended horizon, but we soon sank down into the valleys between them and had nothing in view but the wall of waters around us. The Master of the Cartel pointed out to me an object which he now and then saw on the edge of the horizon as a french privateer but I could not perceive it. Towards the afternoon the sailors began to look out for land and at length descried it but too late in the day to allow hopes of entering the port that evening and the Moon had risen before we got up to it. As no vessels are allowed to enter after dark we were obliged to anchor outside and remain another night tossed about on the waters. The evening was very fine but cold. I found the deck however a better place than the cabin.

Tuesday 19th. As soon as day was well introduced our vessel moved and passing the castle which stands at the mouth of the harbour to defend it moved up the long and perplexed passage. - We here had our first view of France and it was not at all calculated to impress a stranger with a high opinion of the country though perhaps regret for home may influence first feelings. One side of the harbour was barren the other hilly and green with trees and shrubs and here and there a little white house varied the landscape. About 11 o clk we passed a guard ship stationed at the upper end of the harbour and then came to anchor. I was now in hopes of going on shore but understood that no one could leave the ship until the arrival of an officer from the town of Morlaix to examine us and give permission to land. To expedite this event some one was dispatched from the guard ship and during the delay we breakfasted. Afterwards we amused ourselves with observing the manouvres of the men on board the guard ship and listening to the laughable observations of our cabin boy. Late in the afternoon the mighty man of office came attended by several understrappers and a barge full of Frenchmen apparently beggars and porters. A formal examination then ensued - One of the officers came to me and taking my hat off he first searched it and then laid it on the deck he then felt my pockets my breast my sides and cloaths and lastly desired to look into my shoes after which I was permitted to pass. A similar ceremony was performed on all the strangers and though I felt surprised at such a singular reception I could hardly help laughing at the ridiculous nature of their precautions. Our english sailors looked on with pity and indignation which was not diminished by the seizure of some letters written in the harbour and given to the captain of the cartel to be conveyed back to Plymouth and by the post to our friends in London. These letters however were all seized and conveyed to Morlaix and we were not allowed to write home of our arrival in France.[6]

The various parts of the carriage the boxes packages &c being placed on deck word was given and immediately the crew of frenchmen pounced on them and conveyed them in every direction and by the most awkward and irregular means into the barge alongside and this with such an appearance of hurry and bustle such an air of business and importance and yet so ineffectually that sometimes nine or ten men would be round a thing of a hundred pounds weight, each most importantly employed and yet the thing would remain immovable until the crew were urged by their officer or pushed by the cabin boy. At last all was placed in the barge & then leave was given to the cartel to return and certainly it was with no pleasurable feeling I beheld myself separated from my countrymen; that I saw them returning and felt concious of the tyrannical and oppressive laws and manners of the people in whose hands we remained but things being as they were I endeavoured to content and amuse myself by looking out for variety in the manners of the people around me.

The delay occasioned by the forms of office had made it too late to reach Morlaix with the tide just returning I therefore laid myself down by the carriage until about 11 o clk at which time I was told we should move.

About 9 oclock this evening whilst lying aground I observed several luminous spots about the size of peas which gradually became visible in the mud. They increased in brightness at first but in a few minutes their splendour decreased it frequently however increased and decreased alternately for some time; now and then they disappeared entirely but

---

6   But a letter which Davy apparently sent home at this time is quoted in his brother's biography (John Davy, **Memoirs of the life of Sir Humphry Davy**, 1836, p.4).

would frequently reappear again but at last they all became invisible. They were motionless during the whole of the time.

Towards 11 o clk our barge was afloat and we began to move up the river. The moon was up but frequently obscured by clouds when she afforded light enough to make the banks distinctly visible they appeared very pretty, they were high in general and well wooded. At last we got into the town and I left the barge to the care of the officer who had been stationed in it by Moreau[7] at the transferance of the goods from the cartel and proceeded with a guide to the Inn.

I could see nothing at this hour ($\frac{1}{2}$ past 12 o clk) but what the lantern of my guide illuminated. That however was not calculated to enchant me with the place; - there was no footpath; there was plenty of mud and no means of avoiding it; and on getting to the Hotel there was one of the dirtiest pig-sties I ever saw. I had been informed that Morlaix was a very indifferent town for accomodation but nevertheless had formed a respectable idea of it and therefore on following a horse in at the house door of the hotel imagined we had mistaken the place but I found unfortunately that my guide was correct and as I perceived my opinion would not be heightened by further investigation I sat down without consideration in very hungry plight to supper. It was clean and with my appetite its quality was no object and being also considerably fatigued I had no difficulty in going to sleep though singularly accomodated.

Wednesday 20th. Morning being arrived we breakfasted in a manner which though it well deserved notice I leave, to commemorate our examination at the Douane or Custom house which immediately followed it. I should first observe that the officers had permitted us to take out of the seat boxes &c in their presence what was absolutely necessary for the night and in the morning we went to claim the rest. I found the carriage &c in the barge just as they had been left and the officer still there. The Douane was not yet open and we had to wait patiently or otherwise for some time looking on our things but not daring to touch them. At last business commenced. The officers having arranged themselves on the edge of the quay some thirty or forty inhabitants of the town ran and tumbled down the steps and leaping into the barge seized some one thing some another and conveyed them to the landing place above. This sight alone was a curious one for they being totally destitute of all method and regularity it seemed as if a parcel of thieves was scampering away with what was not their own. - The body of the carriage was the part which most embarrassed them for as there were no cranes or any substitute for them on the quay it was necessary that mere hand labour should perform the important task of raising it to the place above. This was an effort of great magnitude but they

---

7   Commissaire de Police at Morlaix.

manfully surmounted it and our fears of seeing the carriage resigned to its fate at the bottom of the stairs were fortunately unfounded.

All this being done these gentry formed a ring and the officers began their work all the boxes & packages even to the tool chest were taken out and conveyed into the house and then some getting inside and some mounting outside they searched all the corners and crannies for what they could find and thumped over every part of the carriage to discover hollow and secret places. Finding nothing like concealment they entered the house and began to operate on the trunks and as they were disappointed in their hopes of booty from the carriage they seemed determined to make up for their loss here. Package after package was opened roll after roll unfolded each pair of stockings unwrapped and each article of apparel shaken but still being disappointed in their hopes of a pretext for seizure they at last laid claim to two or three dozen of cotton stockings because they were new and it was long before the arguments of their being necessary for a long journey and of their being marked was sufficient to induce them to render them up again. At last the business ended with every thing in the possession of the rightful owners and a gift to the officers for their polite attentions.

As soon as this examination was concluded leave was given for the carriage to be put together and the goods replaced in it. The first set of men now found work again and I was astonished how with their poor means and their want of acquaintance with such affairs they were still able to get it in order 'tis true they made the job appear a mighty one but they got through it and after having exclaimed "levez"; "levez"; for an hour or two every thing was in a moveable state and horses being tied to we proceeded in order to the Hotel.

I shall refrain from making comments upon this peculiar examination except to remark that if variety be one of the traveller's pleasures we have certainly enjoyed a very high one this morning for the whole affair was so different to anything that I had before witnessed that I cannot possibly charge it with a monotonous effect. The occurrence was one which will ever make this day signal in my remembrance.

Thursday 21st. - How long we are to enjoy the pleasures of this delectable place is uncertain for until the Governor has received certain instructions respecting us we are fixed. I suppose he has to learn whether the government continues in the same mind now, that they were in when they sent Sir H Davy his passport to England if it does not we of course are prisoners.

I have been wandering into the town today for though there is sufficient in the house to surprise me at every turn yet I wished to see the general appearance of things. I find them however all alike and I cannot refrain from calling this place the dirtiest and filthiest imaginable. - The streets are paved from house to house with small sharp stones no particular part being appropriated to foot passengers. The kennels are full of filth and generally close to the house. The places and corners are occupied by idle loiterers who cloathed in dirt stand doing nothing and the houses - but I will endeavour to describe our hotel. - This (the best in the place) has but one entrance and it is paved in a manner similar to the streets; through it pass indiscriminately horses pigs poultry human beings or whatever else has a connection with the house or the stables and pigsties behind it. - On the right hand of the passage and equally public as a thoroughfare with it is the kitchen here a fire of wood is generally surrounded by idlers beggars or nondescripts of the town who meet to warm themselves and chatter to the mistress and they hold their stations most tenaciously though the processes of cooking are in progress. - I think it is impossible for an English person to eat the things that come out of this place except through ignorance or actual and oppressive hunger and yet perhaps appearances may be worse than the reality for in some cases their dishes are to the taste excellent and inviting but then they require whilst on the table a dismissal of all thoughts respecting the cookery or kitchen. - to proceed: On the left of the passage is a dining room ornamented with gilded chairs tables & frames but with broken windows and stone floors. At the end of the passage stairs pass up to the rooms above and an opening to the yard and outhouses and these are so much alike in appearance that if pigs do not go up stairs at least animals as dirty do. - The chambers are the most respectable parts of the house and approach nearest to cleanliness but the striking deficiency of every thing like comfort indeed the evident disregard of that requisite is so prominent that I think a native of any other place but this must look with a very dissatisfied eye at the accomodations.

Leaving the house I was much better pleased with the garden; but to get to which the previous penance of crossing the yard was necessary. At this season of the year the garden is not so interesting from its contents as from its situation. A rough and rugged rock rises abruptly behind the house to a great height. The little prominences and ledges on the side of this rock are covered with soil and cultivated and paths have been made in a rude manner from one spot to another. The scenery here is very varied and romantic and the arbours standing on the points of projections present singular and beautiful views of the town. The garden is still green but there is little of beauty in it except its peculiar situation.

I had the curiosity to try on a pair of <u>sabots</u> or wooden shoes an article which appears to be universally adopted in this town. Each shoe is made out of one piece of wood and as the cavity intended for the foot is generally too large the space unoccupied when the shoe is on is filled with hay. As my foot did not agree well with its wooden case I soon gave up my experiment but the inhabitants walk about for hours together apparently without feeling the incumbrance at their feet. A pair of sabots I should think would weigh more than 4 lbs. Some intended for les dames are more delicately cut out than the others they are moreover neatly ornamented above and below with nails and scorched here and there to give variety in colours.

Friday 22nd. This morning we were at liberty to leave Morlaix and as it contains nothing that can induce a voluntary stay we gladly bade farewell to it. - We travelled by the Post which is very bad in this country. The horses are very well individually but of the four attached to our carriage no two were alike either in size or qualities this however is no objection here for in connecting them with the carriage such a dis-union is made among them that it is not necessary that they should act in concert and accordingly they very seldom do. They <u>have</u> collars and were they made of leather there is matter enough in one to make four in the English fashion but the principal and useless part is wood the necessary and important part leather and straw and the ornamental part either a plume of feathers a weathercock or a set of bells. Ropes tied to these collars are also made fast to the carriage by knots as being easily made over again when the ropes break. They are preserved from <u>very frequently</u> getting under the horses feet by small cords which pass from one to the other across the back of the horse. The carriage horses are tied to the bar the fore horses to the end of the pole and the cords are generally so long that a space of six feet intervenes between the front & hind pairs. I actually observed this morning that we proceeded for a distance of nearly two miles without any one horse coming nearer to another than four feet.

The saddle horse besides the simple trappings described above has also some very peculiar and important pieces of furniture first a saddle sometimes of a moderate size but generally very high to this is frequently suspended a pair of jack boots but of these anon secondly a bridle which however is found so different in its form and structure at different post houses and even at the same that no character but that of variety will attach to it (it is to be observed that the other horses have something of this kind) and thirdly the great coat by no means an unimportant part either in use or appearance for being mounted on the peak in front of the saddle it has an aspect of great dignity and it is generally so disposed by the rider as to mend the rough uneven seat afforded him by his saddle.

The postillion deserves a paragraph to himself. - He is mostly a young always a lively man. His dress with the exception of his boots and that part which covers his head varies infinitely but hairy jackets appear to be frequent as outer garments and they are often finely ornamented. At other times the dress seems to be a kind of uniform being at many post houses together of one colour and turned up at the edge with another. The first pair of Jack boots that I saw came out of the kitchen of the hotel at Morlaix for as it is almost impossible for a man when in them to move about by his own exertions the postillion had left them in the above named place until all was arranged at the carriage but then he used his reserved strength and showed them off in a walk from the fire side to the horses. - They appeared like two very large cylinders of leather terminated at the end by purses for the feet; they rose about six inches above the knee and were cut away at the back part to admit the use of that joint. Their external diameter was about 7 inches but the cavities within were not much too large for the legs. The sides of the boots consisted of two or three folds of strong leather sewed together and stuffed on the inside with wool to the thickness of ¾ of an inch and sometimes more and the lower part or foot not being stuffed in the same way was much smaller in proportion though being still too large it was made perfect by a wisp of straw. - The weight of a pair of Jack boots varies between 14 and 20 lbs generally. - These boots are sometimes moved about by the postillions independant of the exertions of the horses and then an enormous pair of stirrups are hung to the saddle to sustain them in riding at other times they are attached to the saddle by straps and the postillion jumps on to his horse and into them at the same time. - The use of them according to the wearers is to save their legs from being broken should the horses stumble or the carriage be overturned and though a traveller must laugh at the sight of such clumsy things there is not much amusement in the idea that the people who best know their horses and drivers conceive such a precaution constantly necessary.

Other appendages to the Postillion are the whip and the tobacco pouch. The first is a most tremendous weapon to dogs pigs and little children. With a handle of about 30 inches it has a thong of 6 or 8 feet in length and it is constantly in a state of violent vibratory motion over the heads of the horses giving rise to a rapid succession of stunning sounds. The second is generally a bag though sometimes a pocket exclusively appropriated answers the purpose. It contains tobacco a short pipe a flint a steel german tinder[8] and sometimes a few rareties. To this the postillion has constant recurrence and whilst jogging on will light his pipe and smoke it out successively for several hours.

The progress made by this kind of equipage is very bad and particularly on such sad roads as we have had to pass over to day. The ropes alias the reins traces bridle stirrup straps &c are continually breaking and though the postillion sometimes manages to mend them without stopping yet with all his care and the travellers impatience he has to halt and dismount two or three times in an hour.

On leaving Morlaix we ascended a hill and then came on to a level country above. The weather has been bad for some time and the roads are very dirty but they are also so bad that it was more pleasant to walk than be bumped about with the carriage. We put up some time after dark at a town called I think Guingamp.

Saturday 23rd, - The scenery has been much prettier today than it was yesterday it is more woody and presents greater variety of forms. The roads also improve. Towards the middle of the day we had a sight of the sea at a distance on the left hand and the whole prospect was here

---

8   German tinder or amadou is prepared from certain fungi found on trees.

very fine. Yesterday and the early part of this morning presented an open country in apparently a poor state of cultivation and very little land seemed to be inclosed.[9] The huts on the road side were miserable places and the inhabitants appeared to be in an equally wretched state indeed as yet I have seen nothing approaching at all to the Arcadian in its nature except what nature furnishes. The country we have passed through this afternoon appeared more luxuriant though less inhabited. The forests were in many parts quite thick and penetrated by nothing but the road; in other places however spots had been cleared & cultivated and from the effect of the surrounding scenery presented some of the most picturesque views imaginable. - We are at present housed in the little village of Lambelle[10] and I am in hopes shall sup well & sleep comfortably for the kitchen and the chambers have promising appearances.

The dessert which is a constant attendance upon dinner and supper is an agreeable foretaste of the pleasures to be enjoyed in the more southern countries during the fruit season. Grapes are a very regular and excellent dish. - During the vintage they select the finest bunches and stringing them suspend them from the ceiling of a dry room in this situation they shrink a little but do not undergo further alteration for some time. They are thus constantly placed on the table and are very good.

Sunday 24th, - Today we continued to advance towards Paris wishing to get there as soon as possible but the badness of the roads and the driving is a great retardation. The woody scenery has been very fine today but attended with a great deficiency of civilised appearance.

This evening I for the first time saw a glow worm. The night was very dark (about 7 o clk) and one of our horses had tumbled over; this accident destroyed the traces and whilst the postillion were renovating them I saw the little insect by its light amongst the horses feet in the middle of the road. Two small luminous spots were visible upon it but the light was very weak. I picked the worm up and secured[?] it until we were again in a moving state and then amused half an hour by observing its appearance. The lights had disappeared but soon became visible and then shewed a varying intensity for some minutes but soon entirely disappeared. On examining it afterwards at Rennes I found it to be a small black worm not three fourths of an inch in length and having no parts particularly distinguished as those which had been luminous. It was dead and must have been in a very weak state when I found it.

Tired of the darkness of the night and badness of the roads I was glad when I saw the lights of Rennes at a distance and more so as their appearance was such as to make us suppose we were approaching a large

---

9 The enclosure of open fields, begun in the sixteenth century to improve agriculture, was almost complete in Britain by 1813. By contrast, Brittany was one of the most backward provinces of France.

10 Lamballe.

town a thing we had not yet seen in France. About half past eight we entered the city and from the length of streets which we traversed between the gate and the post house judged it to be of considerable size. The streets were lighted up here and there at some of the corners but on the whole were very dark and dismal. - At the Post house we found poor accomodations but not being able to get better were obliged to accept them, - The supper was good but the place very cold and desolate and from being built of stone from containing long galleries winding stone stairs narrow passages deserted rooms &c strongly reminded me of the interior of a romantic castle and a black man as cook attendant &c wonderfully assisted the fancy.

Monday 25th, - We did not leave Rennes this morning until past 10 o Clock but I saw nothing of this capital of [ ]^{11} except the place before the Post house and the streets through which we passed. It does not appear externally very much better than Morlaix except that being far larger it can supply a greater variety of things and admits the possibility of getting any reasonable thing that may be desired. - There was abundance of the dried or rather hung fruit that we had found in the towns through which we had passed and it is an excellent accomodation for with bread it forms an excellent and pleasant article of food which may always be eaten without any of those difficulties arising from suppositions respecting the mode of preparation adopted with respect to viands.

The town of (Laval ?) is that which has received us this evening and its appearance considered in connection with that of Rennes marks progressive improvement in every thing as we advance towards the Capital of the Empire.

The coldness of the weather makes one as soon as housed run to the fire for warmth and as the kitchen is the general apartment inhabited by the family it is mostly the only place which contains one ready made. The fuel in all those parts of the country through which we have yet passed is exclusively wood and charcoal and it is here in abundance from the immense tracts of Land covered by forests. A fire place is a space inclosed by the projecting sides and throat of a chimney generally so large that several persons may conveniently stand inside of it. The fire is made on the stone or brick floor iron dogs being used to raise the first faggots inflamed that air may pass beneath. These fires when good are cheerful and comfortable but expensive and therefore when not required for cooking or the use of customers are generally covered up with the ashes and left to burn in a smothering manner which they will do for a long time. - That travellers may not burn too much wood in their apartments for which however they constantly pay dearly they are

---

11   Prior to the Revolution Rennes was the capital of Brittany. It then became the administrative centre of the department Ille et Vilaine.

generally supplied with it in a green state so that the bellows are continually necessary - but they are very seldom to be found.

Tuesday 26th - We left Laval before breakfast this morning and were afterwards sorry we had done so. About 11 o Clk that meal became necessary but we could meet with no accomodations to get it. - We now found the utility of english contrivance and resorted with success to a travelling tea-kettle and caddy. Contributing the tea sugar and kettle on our part, we were able to heat some water at a Post house at which we stopped and making milk from the yolk of eggs[12] produced the necessary beverage. Bread was deficient and not liking that of the house we sought for some at a bakers shop where it was found of an excellent quality. - Thus luckily our fears of fasting were removed and we were reinstated in a travelling condition. - But the difficulties we had met with made me resolve never in future to be unprovided for such a juncture.

The day's posting brought us through a very fine country to Alençon at which place we put up for the night and had reason to be well satisfied with the accomodations. The attentions we met with were more civilized and disinterested than any that had before been given to us in France.

Wednesday, 27th. We have had beautiful weather throughout the whole day and such an air of spirit and chearfulness was thrown by it over the country and every object it contained as to make it one of the most amusing days I have passed since we left home.

There appears to me to be a multitude of small villages in this part of the country more in proportion by far than in England but then their appearance is such as almost to make one wish them away. Those I allude to contain perhaps each from 40 to 60 or 80 huts now and then more sometimes less. The circumstance of their being connected together does not appear to impress the inhabitants with an idea that any general accomodations are required. There is no pavement, indeed the roads are worse in those villages than in the open country from the circumstance of more labour being done on them. There is no communication from house to house no approch to civilization above their insulated countrymen and apparently no performance of any thing in common except gossiping. Now and then you will find a bakers shop in them and at times a wine-seller's but in general each one seems to supply all his wants by his own exertions or from the nearest great town and to do no more.

I have been much surprised at this because at first I imagined that what I could not get at the huts on the road might be obtained at the next village but in this I have frequently been disappointed and have often

---

12   No other written reference was found to this use of egg, but my wife's grandfather always had a raw egg instead of milk stirred into his breakfast tea. BB

found a better shop for bread fruit wine &c in a little dwelling along by the road side and at a distance from towns than in these villages, - There is indeed very little difference in the accomodations you are able to obtain at french huts whether they are collected together in villages or dispersed over the country and the improvement that would be supposed to take place on the union of a number of persons on one spot appears here to be wanting. Perhaps this may in part be accounted for by the deplorable state of their habitations and their constant employment abroad. They make no other use of their huts than as mere shelters from the wind and weather (It is evident bare walls afford as much protection in this way as if they were covered with damask) and their lives at least the conscious and active part of them may be considered as spent rather in the open air than in doors so that the advantage of internal improvements will not be so often suggested to their minds as it would be supposing a degree of subordination to be established in which case some individuals would have less field occupation and more homely cares to attend to - but whatever may be the cause I was at first very much struck by the appearance.

The old adage of <u>Good wine needs no bush</u> is often called to mind by the thirstiness of the postillions and the houses of refreshment. <u>Le vin ordinaire</u> is the common drink of the people and as we approach Paris increases in use. Cider is a general beverage but beer is wanting. On the roadside and in the towns there are many houses for the refreshment of passengers where wine is sold it is frequently the only article to be obtained but sometimes in the same house with it are to be gotten bread and fruit. In the small towns and on the road side it is the custom to indicate these houses by a large green bough fixed over the door or thrust out of the window but I have now & then observed a house containing many casks and drawing a large trade among the neighbours and passengers without any mark of this kind and from the apparently faithful adherence of the postillions to these houses and the numbers continually to be found inside have reason to believe that the wine within is so good as to need no bush.

To night we rest at Dreux (I think) and hope to reach Paris tomorrow:

Thursday 28th. - I cannot help dashing a note of admiration to one thing found in this part of the country - the Pigs! - At first I was positively doubtful of their nature for though they have pointed noses long ears rope like tails and cloven feet yet who would have imagined that an animal with a long thin body back and belly arched upwards lank sides long slender feet and capable of outrunning our horses for a mile or two together could be at all allied to the fat sow of England. When I first saw one (which was at Morlaix) it started so suddenly and became so active in its motions on being disturbed and so dissimilar in its actions to our swine that I looked out for a second creature of the same kind before I ventured to decide on its being a regular animal or an extraordinary production of nature but I find they are all alike and that what at a distance I should judge to be a greyhound I am obliged on a near approach to acknowledge a pig.

We today entered on the wine country though not on a district at all famous for its produce. Wine is here more abundant though perhaps not better, - The orchards are very numerous and as we approached to Paris the roads were bordered by abundance of apple trees on which the fruit hung in great quantities.

The roads improve very much as they approach the capital and indicate advancement to a frequented district. They are paved in the middle from Paris to an extent of 20, 30 and 40 miles outwards continuously and are in general preserved in excellent repair. They are very straight so that there is but little variety in the view presented in passing along them. A road will go in a straight line for four or five miles and then on turning an angle another length equal to the former presents itself so that as the eye is enabled to perceive at once all it will see for the next hour the expectation slackens and a monotonous effect is produced.

On getting within a few miles of Paris this effect ceases and a finer replaces it for the towns become frequent and large and with the occurrence of country seats and villas cause the road to bend & produce greater variety. The artificial scenery also is more varied and interesting.

At Versailles we seemed completely to have left behind us the tract of country which for six days has occupied us and to have entered into the moving busy and civilized world. Here every thing was grand. The houses were fine and regular the gardens numerous & beautiful the streets long large well paved and full of people and the Palace of which we had a front view whilst changing horses magnificent. - Our stay here was not more than a quarter of an hour and we were not long before we arrived at the more important place of Paris.

The first impression made on my mind by a sight of this city was that there was much to commend and admire and also much to be reprobated and disapproved of. - I reserve my opinion however for a future view of it and as we shall remain here some time opportunities to form it will be afforded in abundance.

We have got into a house called Hotel d'Autriche but where I cannot imagine we shall stop. It is deficient in common accomodations and yet withal it bears a very respectable character.

Friday 29th - I am here in the most unlucky and irritating circumstances possible. Set down in the heart of Paris that spot so long so desiringly looked at & so vainly too from a distance by numbers of my countrymen. I know nothing of the language or of a single being here added to which the people are enemies & they are vain. My only mode will be to stalk about the town looking and looked at like a man in the monkish catacombs. My mummies move however and they see with their eyes: I must exert myself to attain their language so as to join in their world.

Saturday, 30[13]th. I saw the Galerie Napoleon[13] to day but I scarcely know what to say of it. It is both the Glory and the disgrace of France. As being itself and as containing specimens of those things which proclaim the powers of man and which point out the high degree of refinement to which he has risen it is unsurpassed unequalled and must call forth the highest and most unqualified admiration. But when memory brings to mind the manner in which the works came here and views them only as the gains of violence and rapine she blushes for the people that even now glory in an act that made them a nation of thieves.

The Museum contains paintings statues pieces of sculpture and casting of which by far the greater number have been brought from Italy. They are the works of the old and most eminent masters and it is a collection of chef-d'oeuvres. The statues are arranged in the lower part of the Louvre in many saloons of great magnificence. There are amongst them the Apollo the Laocoon The Venus de Medicis the Hercules the Gladiator dying and many more of the finest pieces of the ancient Greek Masters.[14] The paintings are placed in a Gallery of enormous length and arranged in schools as the Flemish school the Dutch school the French school &c. It contains some thousands of pieces. Free admission is given to all parts of this National establishment and more particularly to foreigners. Indeed it seems to be a principle with the French Government to admit strangers with as much facility as possible to all public property not interfering or not directly connected with their political affairs.

Returning from the Gallery I passed by the triumphal arch[15] erected to commemorate the many and signal victories of the Emperor. It is a beautiful structure formed of the rarest and most valuable marbles. Many of the pieces came from Italy having been taken from the situations in which the ancient Romans had placed them.

From this Arch I went to the column erected to the honor of Napoleon in the Place Vendome. It is formed of the Artillery taken from the Austrians during the campaigns of the years [   ] and is an imitation of the columns of Antonine and Trajan at Rome. It is covered with bass reliefs representing those actions and deeds of the Emperor worthy to be transmitted to posterity.[16] A colossal statue of him also of metal is placed

---

13   Now the Grande Galerie of the Musée du Louvre.
14   All the statues listed here were returned to Italy after the fall of Napoleon. The Medici Venus, now in the Uffizi Museum, Florence, is not to be confused with the Venus de Milo, acquired by the Louvre in 1821.
15   L'Arc de Triomphe du Carrousel, erected in 1806-1808 to commemorate the victories of Napoleon in 1805.
16   La Colonne d'Austerlitz, surmounted by a statue of Napoleon by Chaudet, was made of bronze from nearly 1250 cannons taken from the Russians and Austrians during the 1805 campaign.

on the top. I ascended it carrying a candle in my hand by an internal winding staircase: and had a fine view of Paris from the Gallery at the top. When the pillar was made the founder cheated the government i.e. the Emperor by melting down with the artillery a great quantity of baser metal; the fraud was discovered when too late except to make the rogue refund his ill gotten gains.

Monday. Nov. 1st. Walked in the Thullieries for an hour or two: found them very pretty and full of people. They extend along the bank of the Seine from the Palace of the Thullieries to the Place de Concord.[17] The garden abounds with statues fountains and raised terraces. It is the Parisian lounge and is much frequented.

The Seine is a very poor dirty river not at all what I expected to find it. It has of course no tide and is therefore almost unfit for navigation at least such as is required by a large city. Scarcely any thing moves on it but charcoal barges and washing houses. The barges come down from the upper country to supply Paris with fuel.

There are many bridges over the Seine at Paris thirteen I believe and some of them fine structures. Between the Institute on one side and the Louvre on the other there is one of iron but it is for foot passengers only. Le Pont des Arts is a good stone bridge crossing the river at the head of the Thullieries. Le Pont de (Jena ?)[18] passes from the Place de Concord to the Senate house. It is a new work. Le Pont neuf is an old bridge or rather two bridges for it touches in the middle on the corner of an island. It is under repair but the works stand still at present for want of money.

There are many smaller bridges running across to the island in the Seine on which part of Paris is situated. There is nothing particular in them except their vicinity[;] in one part three occur in less than 100 yards.

Tuesday 2nd. The streets of Paris are in general narrow. At the same time there are many of great length and width and noble appearance but the number is not so great as might be expected in a city so much vaunted. Many of them make crooked lines and there are a vast number of irregular corners and angles. - The quays and the boulevards are the greatest ornaments in the way of communication in the city. The quays continue on both sides of the river through the whole town except about the island where the houses in some places advance close to the water. When they are open they form fine promenades for the Parisians and more particularly towards the Louvre and the Gardens for the traffic in charcoal being all done at the other end of the city and no other

---

17   Les Tuileries and La Place de la Concorde.
18   The iron footbridge is le Pont des Arts. The stone bridge is le Pont Royal (then
      called le Pont des Tuileries). The new bridge is le Pont de la Concorde. Le Pont d'
      Iéna is further downstream.

business worthy notice being done on the river there is nothing to disturb the loungers. A slight wall breast high runs along the edge of the river to prevent accidents.

There are two circles of boulevards the inner and the outer and each of them goes round the city at different distances from the centre (the Louvre). They may be described as two great circumscribing roads of which the broad and generally gravelled part is over-shadowed by high trees planted on each side. During the summer and autumn these trees give a refreshing shade which invites an immense number of persons willing to walk but not in the heat of the sun to promenade under them. Shops stalls coffee houses and various places of public amusement line the sides and present a light airy pleasant and inviting variety.

There are not many fine places at Paris. La Place Vendome La Place de concord &c are among the best.

The streets of Paris are paved with equality that is to say no difference is made in them between men & beasts and no part of the street is appropriated to either[;] add to this that the stones of which the pavement consists are very small and sharp to the foot and I think much more need not be said in praise of it. - At this season also besides the pain caused by this sort of pavement an additional inconvenience arises from it for though in fine weather a walker may make up his mind to skip across a street half a dozen times in the length of it to avoid the carriages that drive down upon him, and from which he has no other means of saving himself yet when in frosty weather the sink has become choaked up and the street is overflowed by the never ceasing fountain he feels averse to plunge himself into a pond though to save himself from a carriage and when he does do so he generally adds energy to the desperation required by an exclamation.

Speaking of carriages I well notice that our hackny coaches are here supplied by a set of cabriolets which go with a single horse. These are very cheap but the men drive furiously and make streets already dangerous from the absence of foot paths still more so.

Thursday 4th. Whilst passing through the court of the Louvre I stopped a few moments to see the men now at work in cleaning repairing and N-ing it. The Louvre is a square building with a large central court opening on the four sides to the place the Quay & the streets which surround it by large arched ways and it is allowed to be a thoroughfare to persons on foot who have no parcels with them.

Time had so blackened this building that it was difficult to tell the material of which it was formed except that the architecture and work declared it stone but certainly without close inspection Marble Porphyry &c would not have been suspected. The modern labours are intended to bring these into view and fully answer the end proposed. Already part of the interior displays a beauty and variety of colour and design previously not supposed to exist in the building. - As they go they continue to make additions to the original parts by sticking up N's in every spot central and lateral where they can. This is a principle scrupulously attended to in every public work. The Museum the Gallery &c abound with N's and silently recal the Emperor to mind at every step and turn.

This palace is situated on the bank of the river. The Place de Carousal[19] is interposed between it and the Thullieries but the two buildings are connected on the Seine side by the Long Picture Gallery before mentioned.

Sunday 7th. The two things by which a Frenchman particularly distinguishes Sunday from a week day are first by a certain extra number of prayers said either at home or at church and secondly by making it a day of pleasure instead of work. Now neither of these things interfere with or prohibit them from opening their shops and accordingly you will find the streets as gay on such a morning as this as on any other morning and without a good memory or an almanack it would be difficult to tell the Sabbath from other days for no visible distinctions exist. In the evening, 'tis true, they shut up their shops earlier and by this you may be led to suppose when the day is nearly over what is has been but why do they shut them up? - to go to the Theatre "for" said a frenchman to me "every Theatre is open tonight" - and that "<u>every</u>" includes some that are open only on Sunday evenings.

The churches are open all day but they are open also on other days and I did not see more in them than usual. A parisian laughed at me for expecting more.

Tuesday 9th. I went to day to La Prefecture de Police for a passport for it is not allowed to any but an inhabitant of Paris and whose name is registered as such to be in the city without one. I found the place out on the bank of the river an enormous building containing an infinity of offices and it was only by paying for information that I found out the one I wanted. On entering it I beheld a large chamber containing about twenty clerks with enormous books before them and a great number of people on the outside of the tables all of whom came on business respecting passports. Mine was a peculiar case and soon gained attention for excepting Sir H. Davy's there was not another free Englishman's Passport down in their books. An American who was there and (perceiving me at a loss for French) had spoken to me would scarcely believe his senses when he saw them make out the paper for a free Englishman and would willingly have been mighty inquisitive - After having numbered the passport and described me in their books with a round chin a brown beard a large mouth a great nose &c &c they gave me the paper and let me go. - It was a call upon all magistrates and authorities in Paris to respect aid &c - but the article which pleased me most as having a great appearance of liberality was, that as a stranger

---

19   La Place du Carrousel.

who had not always opportunities I was to be admitted on showing the paper to all public property as Museums Libraries on any day though the public are admitted to many of them but two and three times a week.

Thursday 11th. - I went to day with Sir H D to La Bibliotheque Imperial[20] the great National Library and I think it is worthy of being national property.   It contains an immense number of books in all languages and on all subjects arranged in several long galleries separated into divisions. Many of these divisions or rooms have tables down the middle with chairs & forms round them and pens ink and paper on them. The doors are open on every day except Sundays between the hours of 9 and 2. Any person of a decent appearance may go in and have any book on applying to the librarians who are in attendance. These must be read there but by a proper application to the principal Librarian books may be had away to be returned in a certain number of days.

There is also in the same building a collection of scarce MSS but they are preserved in rooms below and are shown with much caution. Another room not generally open contains a variety of antiquities.

In the centre of one of the galleries is a brasscast[21] (by [   ]) of the French Parnassian Hill. It has in various positions about it figures of the celebrated French authors accompanied by the muses. The base is about 4 feet wide the height perhaps 3 feet. It is considered a fine piece of workmanship.

In a corner at the meeting of two galleries is a wooden model of the Pyramids of Egypt and the surrounding country.

At the end of the galleries are two globes the largest I believe that have ever been made. They are about 15 feet in diameter. They are placed in a lower story but project up through two large spaces cut in the floor and thus by

[Faraday interrupts the account here, at p.46 of the manuscript. The diary of his 1819 walking tour in Wales occupies pp.49-204. Then the European diary continues with a description of the water supply of Paris (pp.207-341).]

The mode of watering Paris is by fountains and wells. Almost every large house has in the court yard a well with a pulley suspended over it a cord and a bucket. These of course have their water at hand but it happens there are many small houses in the place which have no

---

20   La Bibliothèque Impériale, now la Bibliothèque Nationale.
21   Le Parnasse français, a bronze sculpture, is a model for a monument to the glories of Louis XIV and the great writers of seventeenth-century France commissioned in 1708 from the sculptor Garnier by Titon du Tillet, Commissaire des Guerres. The actual monument was never executed, but the model was bequeathed to the King and eventually placed in the Royal Library, now the Bibliothèque Nationale.

courtyard or well and these give employment to a set of men called water-carriers. These are very busy in the morning. Some have barrels fixed on wheels and drawn either by horses or by themselves and others have pails which they hang on poles and carry on their shoulders. They get water at the fountains and when they have supplied their regular customers they fill the street for a short time with cries of "de l'eau".

The most general form of the fountains is that of a single jet which springs out horizontally from the walls or from posts between knee & breast high. They are extremely numerous some thousands of them exist in Paris in the public places gardens markets and crossings of large streets where they appear to advantage as ornaments much variety and attention is given to their forms. There are two very fine ones in the Boulevards near to which we now live. Basin rises above basin and jet above jet to a great height and not only jets but whole sheets of water sometimes descend from them. The finest specimen of this kind is a fountain near to the Luxembourg Palace. It is an alcove I should think full 50 feet high. The fall of water is in the interior and takes place in a full sheet from the very top it descends into a basin formed below and then passes off to supply the small low jets about the city. Four pillars of stone stand at the distance of 12 or 16 feet from the front to break the uniformity of appearance. An inscription is placed on the building imparting that this fountain was erected by the Emperor &c. It has altogether a very fine and noble appearance and is a great ornament of that part of the city which at first I thought hardly worthy of it. - Many of the simple jet fountains have a thick low wall raised round them for the use of the Parisian washerwomen or as they are more elegantly called Blanchsisseurs[22]. Here they may be seen at all hours scrubbing and thumping the object of their labours until they have half cleaned them and half worn them out but the best display of their abilities is to be seen in the river. In many parts of it old barges have been chained to posts shelving roofs thrown over them the insides furnished with benches the outsides with scrubbing boards and every other requisite necessary to make washing workshops of them. Here sometimes 40 or 50 women may be seen on their knees leaning over the edges of the barge and washing their things in the river. The general course consists of alternations of rincings rubbings and thumpings the last being performed with a thick short bat or flat mallet on a thick stout board, the effect of which may be easily conceived. I must however for the honor of Paris say that I have once seen a woman wash cloaths in a tub with soap but was told that the operation was very uncommon.

Many of the houses here are built of a greyish white calcarious sandstone which often contains vast quantities of shells. I do not know where the stone comes from but am told the distance is not more than 20 miles. The shells are principally spiral univalves and are sometimes so numerous as to produce an evil. The staircase of the hotel we now

---

22   Blanchisseuses - the literal meaning is 'whiteners'.

inhabit is owing to this cause full of small holes. The shells have become loose by the continual treading of people and have been brushed out.

S. 13th   I was this morning disappointed of seeing the sugar manufactories of which there are several round Paris and this disappointment was the greater as their processes differ so much from ours. Having no trading connexion with England or english possessions they have been obliged to get sugar as they could and necessity soon taught them a means of obtaining it from where it had never been looked for in the large way before. Their material is beet root and their product a loaf sugar of good quality though not by any means equal to cane sugar. It is also much higher in price and often stands in the markets at $4\frac{1}{2}$, 5 or $5\frac{1}{2}$ francs (from about $4^s/-$ to $5^s/$) per lb.

S. 14th   I went this morning into some of the churches but was not induced to stop long in any of them. It could hardly be expected that they would have attractions for a tasteless heretic. Some of them were very large and finely ornamented inside and more particularly the altars. Gold shone in abundance and the altar pieces or pictures were by the best masters. Masses were performing in many of them and sometimes two or more in one church at different altars though at the same time. There were many people in some of them but numbers seemed like me to be gazers.   A theatrical air spread through the whole and I found it impossible to attach a serious or important feeling to what was going on.

M. 15th   During a short ramble this morning I came by chance into the Palais Royal and took an easy walk round it. It is a long square building supported on the inside by arcades that run round the whole place. The plot of ground in the middle is gravelled and planted with a few small trees. This palace which was once a private possession is now a collection of public exhibitions coffee houses shops &c and in the evening makes a fine appearance. A series of shops fitted up in a style of much elegance surrounds it beneath the arcades and many coffee houses of great celebrity are interspersed here and there.
I went again in the evening with an Englishman (who had been in France 12 years) and found the appearance of the place completely altered. The attraction was now to the Arcades and the shops. The first were filled with people the second with lights and ornaments. It is the public evening promenade of all the gay Parisians and continues full until a very late hour.   We went into a coffee house said to belong to the handsomest lady in Paris. She is always in the room and is one of the principal attractions. Beside that however the place itself is beautiful. Pillars of marble rise from the floor to the ceiling; glasses and piers line the walls of the room and garlands of flowers run from one to the other. Luxury here has risen to its height and scarcely any thing more refined or more useless can be conceived - I was afterwards cheated into the

Cafe des Aveugles[23] and was rather startled. 'Tis a strange place and very characteristic.

W. 17th Another walk to the Jardine des Plants[24] was as inefficient as before for the purpose of seeing the Museum but I got a fine walk in the Garden and found amusement for some hours. The establishment here forms a kind of college to which several Professors are attached. M Chevreul[25] has distinguished himself in chemistry M Hauy[26] in crystallography M Cuvier[27] in Natural history and there are many other names of note to be found in connexion with these and the establishment.

T. 18 I had occasion to go this morning to M Vauquelin[28] who manufactures chemical preparations for some salts and earths. Whilst they were weighing them I went into the laboratory where several operations were going on. There were two processes the same in kind for the production of oxymuriate of potash.[29]

In these operations they used large earthen-ware vessels. The chlorine was liberated in a large vessel of 11 or 12 gallons capacity which was set in brick work so that a gentle heat could easily be applied. The gas was conducted by a tube from this vessel into a large Woulfes[30] bottle and from thence passed into an earthen ware jar of 6 or 7 gallons capacity which contained the solution of potash. The whole of the salt was found in this vessel and in this respect it differs from the mode adopted in England where in general the gas is made to pass through several different portions of the alkaline solution. From the vessel last mentioned a tube proceeded the end of which was immersed in a jar of water. The common air of the vessels was coming over at the time I was there mixed with a little chlorine. A tube of safety[31] was inserted in the jar containing the solution.

M Dulong[32] the discoverer of the new detonating compound of chlorine and azote is engaged in this laboratory. He was not there at this time but the person in the warehouse spoke of him. He lost an eye by an explosion of the compound at the time that he first discovered it.

I found last night that I had lost my passport. I do not know what the police will say to me about it.

---

23   Café of the Blind, popular at the period of the Revolution. It gained its name from an orchestra of blind musicians recruited from the Hôpital des Quinze-Vingts.
24   Le Jardin des Plantes.
25   Michel Eugène Chevreul (1786-1889), chemist.
26   R. J. Haüy (1743-1822), mineralogist.
27   Baron Georges Léopold Chrétien Frédéric Dagobert Cuvier (1769-1832), comparative anatomist and founder of palaeontology.
28   Nicolas Louis Vauquelin (1763-1829), chemist.
29   Potassium chloride.
30   A large glass vessel.
31   Presumably to prevent the gas pressure building up.
32   Pierre Louis Dulong (1785-1838), discoverer of the Law of Atomic Heats.

F 19 I passed through several markets this morning during my walks and found them all full of people and business. One was the poultry market another the flour market a third was for vegetables and a fourth for meat. They are in general small and roofed over. The corn market is in the open air but to guard against rain and sunshine each stall is overshadowed by an enormous umbrella 9 or 10 feet in width. There is a fine fountain in it.

S. 20th I found my passport today or at least it was found for me and I am fortunately saved much disagreeable trouble.

S 21 A walk along the other side of the river took me by l'Institute the senate house and as far down as the Hospital for Invalids. The Institute of which I hoped to see the inside before this is a very laughable look[?] building on the banks of the river and opposite the iron bridge named des arts. The walls are painted red & yellow from the ground upwards about 18 feet and then the stonework is left to stand the weather. The Senate house is a fine modern stone building with a magnificent portico raised on a flight of steps.[33] It is opposite to the Place de Concord and is a beautiful object in the view of Paris obtained from the Place perhaps the best to be had - The Hospital for Invalids is lower down the river. I merely walked to it and then returned. It is a noble building with large grounds about it. It has a large dome which is entirely gilt on the exterior. It is one of the sights of Paris.

T 23 MM Ampere Clement & Desormes[34] came this morning to shew Sir H Davy a new substance discovered about 2 years ago by M Constant Courtois[35] saltpetre manufacturer. The process by which it is obtained is not as yet publicly known. It is said to be obtained from a very common substance and in considerable quantities.
  A very prominent and remarkable property of this substance is that when heated it rises in vapours of a deep violet colour. This experiment was shewn by the French chemists and also the precipitation of Nitrate of silver by its solution in alcohol. Sir Humphry Davy made various experiments on it with his travelling apparatus and from them he is inclined to consider it as a compound of chlorine and an unknown body.
  It was in small scales with a shining lustre colour deep violet almost black its appearance was very like plumbago. When sublimed it condensed again unaltered into crystals. A very gentle heat is sufficient to volatilize a portion of it for when the bottle containing it was held in the hand the interior soon became of a violet colour. It dissolves very

---

33   The present Assemblée Nationale which then housed the Conseil des Cinq-Cents.
34   André Marie Ampère (1775-1836), celebrated for his contributions to electrodynamics and electromagnetism. Nicolas Clément (1779-1841). Charles Bernard Desormes (1777-1862), politician and scientist who worked on the specific heat of gases.
35   Bernard Courtois, 1777-1838, chemist.

readily in alcohol and forms a solution of a deep brown colour which precipitates nitrate of silver and a portion of the precipitate laid on paper in the sun's light was rapidly discoloured.[36] When a portion of it was rubbed with zinc filings in contact with the atmosphere a fluid combination was formed. When heated with potassium in a glass tube they combined with inflammation. When it was heated in contact with phosphorus a strong action took place & an inflammable gas came over on removing the retort from the mercurial apparatus dense fumes issued from it which seemed to be muriatic acid. They had the same odour and precipitated nitrate of silver in the same way. When the iodine was placed in contact with mercury a combination was gradually formed which on being heated became first orange coloured then black and at last red.

Unfortunately for me I as yet know nothing of the language or I should have learned much more concerning this singular substance but thus I have marked down most of its principle characters. A future day may produce something further about it. Sir Humphry Davy now thinks it contains no chlorine.

W. 24th Being in doors all day I amused myself by noticing in what the apartments we occupy differ from English rooms. The most striking difference in this cold weather is in the fires and fire places. Wood is the universal fuel at least from Morlaix to this place and I understand there are very few places where they burn coals.[37] I have seen coals once and only once they were for some sort of a furnace and not for the apartments. The fires are made on the hearth so that stoves are not wanted. Wood would burn away too rapidly in them. The only things necessary are two iron bars or dogs to raise the ends of the wood that the air may find entrance beneath and through it. If you keep up a cheerful fire it is very expensive and if you keep up a dull fire which is done by smothering up the wood with the ashes it is but a sorry sight. I can never comfortably make a comparison between them and an english coal fire.

From the low position of the fire smokey chimneys are a very common nuisance and are as often found in Palaces as in Huts. It is a thing continually complained of but to remove which efforts are never made.[38]

Charcoal is the usual fuel of the kitchens and almost the whole of the business done on the Seine is with that article. The river is divided between it and the washerwomen.

---

36   The new substance was later called iodine, and Faraday uses the name later in this paragraph. The compound silver iodide decomposes when light falls on it, hence the discolouration. The very similar compound silver chloride was later used for photography.
37   There is very little coal in France and none in Brittany.
38   After being at the Royal Institution Faraday was well aware of Rumford's work on the design of fireplaces to reduce smoking and increase efficiency.

In the internal decoration of apartments the French apply glass and marble two beautiful materials in much greater abundance than the English do. In Brass working also they have risen to great perfection and their application of this material to the construction of ornamental time pieces is exceedingly ingenious and beautiful – In most of the good rooms that I have seen glass has appeared in profusion either as large framed mirrors or as plates of considerable magnitude let into the wall and in some of the coffee houses where decoration has been carried to its utmost bounds. The number is so great & the positions are so judicious that they produce on every side an appearance of infinity.

The marbles used for the purpose of decoration are very fine and apparently numerous. At the Hotel D'Autriche where we before resided there were several beautiful slabs and at this Hotel (des Princes) there is scarcely a table or chest of drawers that is not surmounted by this substance. One beautiful slab is valued at 800 livres it is formed of various minerals arranged mosaically and contains between four and five hundred specimens amongst which are Porphyry Serpentine Marble Sulphate of Baryta Calcareous spar Fluor spar Lapis Lazula Jasper Agate &, &, &. The appearance of the whole being beautiful.

There are also in these apartments three fine large slabs of black encrina marble[39] in one of which was the head of the animal.

To conclude, french apartments are magnificent english apartments are comfortable french apartments are highly ornamental english apartments are clean french apartments are to be seen english apartments enjoyed and the style of each kind best suits the people of the respective countries.

F. 26 I went this evening to the French opera[40] but was not particularly gratified. The building was not what I had expected nor the performance equal to the idea I had formed of it but this I dare say was owing to my ignorance of the language and my want of goût.[41] The theatre was highly ornamented. The illumination of the house was obtained from a large chandelier suspended from the centre of the ceiling over the pit it contained about 80 argand lamps[42] and the same number was in front of the stage. No ladies are allowed in the pit a small part of it near the orchestra which is railed off excepted.

S. 27. A short search in the Booksellers Shops gave me a little idea of the state of the trade in Paris. My object was a French & English grammar but they were scarce not owing to a want of books in general but to a want of communication between the two nations. I at last found one composed for Americans and that answered my purpose. Stereotype

---

39   A marble containing large fossils, favoured for use in buildings.
40   The Opera was housed from 1794-1820 in the Salle Louvois in the Rue de Richelieu.
41   Taste.
42   Oil lamps with a circular wick allowing air up in the centre to give a brighter flame.

printing[43] is in great vogue here and they have many small books beautifully done. The French type is squarer and more distinct than the English.

Books are very cheap here in proportion to English books. I should think on an average they are scarcely half the price and yet large private libraries are seldom met with. Bibliomania is a disease apparently not known in France indeed it is difficult to conceive how their light airy spirits could be subjected to it.

T. 30. I visited the Luxembourg Palace Gallery and gardens to day and find all very beautiful. The building of late called La Palace du Senat Conservateur is in the form of a quadrangle. In the front is an arch or porch in the left side of which is the entrance to the gallery of paintings and the right opens to the grand staircase by which the emperor passes to the Senate. In the furthest part of the building is another porch by which entrance is gained into the gardens. They are very large and are prettily laid out in walks parterres terraces promenades &c and are ornamented with many fountains basins and sculptures.

On shewing my passport at the front porch though not a public day we were admitted to the gallery which contains many of the works of Reubens De la Tour Vernet & Hue and also of David and others. There were Several students at work.

In the gallery called after Reubens the principal paintings are a suite done by him representing particular circumstances of the history of Mary de Medicis and Henry 4th of France. They are considered as chef d'oeuvres of colouring and expression and are invaluable.

In passing from the Gallery of Reubens to that of Vernet we went through a little circular chamber containing some beautiful pieces of sculpture one as large as life the others smaller. - In the gallery of Vernet are several paintings of the different parts of France. - these views are very extensive and some of them contain several hundred figures. They are valuable pictures.

In the Gallery of Rubens is Davids celebrated picture of the three [   ].[44]

W. Dec.1. On this and the preceding days Sir H. Davy made many new experiments on the substance discovered by M. Courtois. This body acts violently upon many of the metals as Iron zinc tin potassium &c and it also combines with potash and combustible bodies. When heated with phosphorus it rapidly unites to it giving off first an inflammable gas and then vapours possessing strong acid properties as the tube cooled the compound formed became solid and of a dark red colour when it was

---

43   Stereotype plates were introduced in the eighteenth century as an economical means
      of preserving pages of type for reprinting. They were cast from moulds made from
      the original forme.
44   Probably 'The oath of the Horatii'.

heated in water it dissolved and the solution was very acid - -When solution of ammonia is poured on to the new substance and left in contact with it for a short time a black powder is formed which when separated dried and heated detonates with great force. - The compound of the substance with iron appears to be decomposed when heated in ammoniacal gas. It is readily soluble in alcohol but not much so in water both solutions precipitate copiously with nitrate of silver and a new product not muriate of silver is produced - This substance when heated effervesces owing possibly to the separation of its water and a fixed body remains fluid at a high temperature but becoming solid when it coold and then in small pieces semitransparent - When fused with potash and then acted on by sulphuric acid it is decomposed and the new substance separates unchanged. - - It unites rapidly with potash and forms a compound which is decomposed by sulphuric and some other acids the substance flying off unchanged - When rubbed with zinc it combined with it and a fluid compound was produced - When heated with iron in a small retort it acted on it with considerable violence and produced a dark coloured compound - nearly the same phenomena were produced by its action upon tin - When heated with potassium it occasioned strong ignition producing the same body as with potash - - M Clement has lately read a paper on it to the Institute in which he says it is procured from the ashes of sea weeds by lixiviation and treatment with sulphuric acid - He conceives it to be a new supporter of combustion.

The discovery of this substance in matters so common and supposed so well known must be a stimulus of no small force to the enquiring minds of modern chemists. It is a proof of the imperfect state of the science even in those parts considered as completely understood. It is an earnest of the plentiful reward that awaits the industrious cultivator of this the most extensive branch of experimental knowledge. It adds in an eminent degree to the beautiful facts that abound in it and presents another wider field for the exercise of the mind. Every chemist will receive it as an addition of no small magnitude to his knowledge and as the forerunner of a grand advance in chemistry.

I was at the house of M Dumotier[45] and saw all his works he is the principal philosophical instrument maker in Paris. I did not see any thing differing very much from the English instruments. There were several air pumps with glass barrels and plates but in general when formed of this material they do not act perfectly. - The Voltas lamps[46] are very pretty & are improved by having a thick ring of zinc at the bottom of the lower vessel and a solution of sulphuric acid in the upper one[;] when the cock is turned to produced the flame in proportion as the gas is thrown out the acid solution sinks into the lower vessel acts upon the zinc

---

45   Louis Joseph Dumotiez, b.1757, and his younger brother, Pierre François, were both instrument makers.
46   Lamps burning hydrogen generated by the reaction of zinc with sulphuric acid and lit by an electric spark.

produced hydrogen and is again returned into the upper vessel so that the lower one is constantly full of gas.

T. 2. The manner of lighting the streets of Paris is very good. They use large lamps which are placed at a considerable distance from each other and high up in the air over the middle of the streets. The mode of suspension appears to be somewhat dangerous though I must say I never heard of an accident. A strong rope is stretched across the street to which another is made fast near the middle this last runs first through a pulley to which the lamp is attached and then through another fixed to the first rope it afterwards passes to the side of the house and then over another pulley down the wall to a little box constantly locked and of which the lamplighter has the key. The lamp has two large burners and three reflectors one behind each burner and the other over them thus throwing all the light in useful directions. This plan is very efficacious but it is sometimes when badly applied partial in its effect.

F. 3. I went to day to the laboratory of M Chevreul at the Jardin des Plants with Sir H. Davy where we remained some time at work on the new substance. I observed nothing particular in this laboratory either as different to the London Laboratories or as peculiarly adapted to the performance of processes or experiments - It was but a small place and perhaps only part of the establishment appropriated to chemistry - I took the Gardens the Pont D'Austerlitz and the Boulevards in my way home and was pleased with my walk though 'twas long and sometimes dirty. The Pont D'Austerlitz is a noble Iron bridge. It has 5 arches springing from stone piers each arch consists of 7 ribs of iron formed by the junctions of frames nearly square and about 3 feet in the side. The distance between the middle of one pier and the middle of the next as well as I could guess it by stepping is about 150 feet and the width of the river I suppose to be 750 feet. The road over the Bridge is excellent and is not excelled by any in Paris. Here is what I have met with no where else in the city except in the Palais Royal and the passages an excellent flag pavement for foot passengers. A toll of a sous is demanded on going on to the bridge.

S. 5 This day is the anniversary of the Emperor's coronation. It is much talked of but more I believe for the gratis admission to all the theatres than for any thing else. Full houses are expected and with reason for on Sundays the houses are always full and the circumstances of no payment will not tend to lessen the number. A partial illumination took place this evening but bad weather was against it.

M. 6. Passed all the morning in the Musée Napoleon. It was observed by an Englishman with whom I went that now these things are in possession of the French people they are full of beauties but before they were all faults.

W. 8. I went to day with Sir H Davy to L'Ecole Polytechnique The National school of chemistry to hear the leçon given to the scholars. It was delivered by M Gay Lussac to about two hundred pupils. The subject was vapour and treated of its formation elasticity compressibility &c. Distribution both by heat and cold was introduced. It was illustrated by rough diagrams and experiments and occupied about an hour. My knowledge of french is so little I could hardly make out the Lecture and without the experiments I should have been entirely at a loss. After the lecture was over we went to see the voltaic battery the expense of which was defrayed by the government.[47] It was comprised in six troughs of wood each containing about 100 pair of plates of 7 or 8 inches square. The troughs were about four feet in length. There was a contrivance at the bottom of each trough by which when a wire was drawn out the acid was let off. This I did not completely understand but the wire appeared to close a long narrow channel which communicated with the bottom of the cells. After looking over the library and a few work rooms I returned home.

Letter to Mother[48]

Thursday, December 9, 1813

Dear Mother,

I write at this time in hopes of an opportunity of shortly sending a letter to you by a person who is now here but who expects soon to part for England. It has been impossible for me to write before since we have been in France but you will have heard of me from Mr Brande and I expect also from Mrs Farquhar. I feel very anxious to know how you are situated in your house and the state of your health but see no mode at present by which you can convey the desired information except by Mr Brande. Sir Humphry told me that when Mr B. wrote to him he would send in the same letter an account of your health and I expect it impatiently. It would be of no use to write a long letter as it is most probable it would not reach you. We are at present at Paris but leave it shortly for the south of France and Lyons will be our next resting-place . . .

I could say much more but nothing of importance and as a short letter is more likely to reach you than a long one I will only desire to be

---

47   An example of Napoleon's support of scientific research.
48   Text from **BJ** 99-100, who notes 'received June 4, 1814'. No MS survives.

remembered to those before mentioned, not forgetting Mr Riebau,[49] and
tell them they must conceive all I wish to say.
Dear Mother, I am with all affection your dutiful son,

M. FARADAY

Mrs M. Faraday, 18 Weymouth Street, Portland Place

Faraday's Journal

T. 9. Passing the old cathedral of Notre Dame to day I stepped in
and found a curious old dirty antique place before me. It is very lofty
long and large. The style of architecture seems to be a rude gothic.
Much old tapestry was hung on the walls near the door but towards the
upper parts things looked in more order. They were performing mass
and many devotees were on their knees before their illuminated tapers.
This circumstance explained to me what I had seen on the outside of the
church where were two women having each a basket of long wax tapers.
Many persons who came up bought a taper and then entered the church.
I found they lighted them in the church and then having given them I
suppose to some Saint they fell to in haste to count their beads. Some I
perceived were much sooner done than others but all left their tapers
burning. They we[re] placed together on the same machine a kind of
wooden horse and a woman who I suppose made an excellent business of
it attended and snuffed them for a small donation. I counted about 50
tapers burning when I came away. I had not time to see the Regalia nor
ascend the tower from whence I was promised the finest view in all Paris.

F 10. A long walk over the Luxembourg gallery and garden
employed all the morning.

S. 11. Sir Humphry Davy had occasion to day for a voltaic pile to
make experiments on the new substance now called iodine and I obtained
one from Mr Chevreul. This pile consisted of circular plates about four
inches in diameter they were united in pairs a zinc & copper plate being
soldered together by the whole of one of their surfaces. They were made
dishing or concave by which means a greater quantity of the solution
used could be retained between them. Twenty four of these double plates
with a solution of muriate of ammonia to which a little nitric acid had
been added produced a good ignition with a little charcoal and platina
wire. This ignition had no effect on the violet coloured gas and as yet it
must be considered as a simple body.

---

49   George Riebau, the bookseller and bookbinder to whom Faraday had been
        apprenticed.

M. 13. To day, I saw the museum at the Jardin des Plants. It is a vast collection of specimens of every kind in Natural History. It was first arranged in a systematic manner by Buffon[50] and is now under the care of M. Cuvier. It occupies two long galleries which are divided into compartments each destined to contain a particular branch of Natural History. It would be useless to point out particular specimens for the whole are beautiful and many singular and the neatness and order of arrangement is very great - The collection of minerals contains very many specimens and there are some very fine specimens. At one end of the same division are deposited those astonishing organic remains discovered by M. Cuvier at Montmartre.

T. 14. Took a walk to day to Montmartre intending to see the place from where were taken the things I saw yesterday. I saw it at a distance only for the Plaister burners who were at work would not let me proceed and I could not explain to them what I wanted - Montmartre is very elevated ground and completely overlooks the City and suburbs. The rock is Limestone and selenite and is burned for plaister on the spot. The place where M. Cuvier discovered the bones &c is a high perpendicular cliff apparently formed at least in part by breaking away the limestone to burn. This stone is very imperfectly crystallized and looks more like a calcarious sandstone it is nearly all soluble in acids. The bones found here are little altered. The phosphate of lime and even the solid animal matter remaining and the form and appearance being unchanged. No infiltration of lime or other earthy matter has taken place.

On looking over Paris from the hill of Montmartre the number of telegraphs[51] catch the eye some of which are always moving in the day time. They are very different to the english telegraphs being more perfect and simple. A strong upright supports on the top a movable cross beam at the ends of which are two others but the arms of these though the same in length and weight are not so in make, one arm of each piece being merely a rim of wood weighted and at a distance is lost to the sight. Small wheels are fixed on the axes which of course move with the arms ropes pass over them and down two sides of the

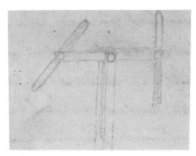

---

50   George Louis Leclerc, Comte de Buffon (1707-1788), encyclopaedist of natural history.
51   An extensive system of semaphore telegraphs extended throughout Napoleon's empire.

upright into the chamber below and by these means the parts are moved and put into different positions. Above 250 figures each perfectly different from the others and easy to be distinguished can be formed by this instrument.

W. 15th I had occasion to go to day to the Bibliotheque Imperiale for some books and finding the room of curiosities open I walked in. It contained a number of medals seals engravings old sculptures and other antiquities. They were not plentiful nor very well arranged but they are said to be valuable. Amongst them I saw a heart of gold with a lable attached to it according to which it had once inclosed the heart of Queen Anne of England.[52]

T. 16. It was some time after I got to Paris before I could make out the occupation of certain men who carry on their backs something like a high tower finely ornamented and painted and surmounted in general with a flag or vane. A flexible pipe proceeded from the lower part of it and a number of cups in a bag hung from the unengaged arm. These men are marchand des every thing that is fit to drink. Some have lemonade in their cisterns these frequent the theatres others have mixed drinks many sell a hot beverage and one that I saw had coffee. They supply those people that cannot do without such refreshments and are too indigent to enter a coffee house and this class includes downwards even as low as the washerwoman of the river. They are frequently about the bridges and very noisy in their calling. - Another curious cry struck my ear on the Pont des Arts a few days ago "Essayez vos forces" said a man behind me and I thought it was some quarrel. On turning round I found he was the possessor of several of Regniers dynamometers[53] and a number of people were about him trying their strength and noting down the results. The man's profession was novel and could not fail of pleasing the Parisians.

S. 18. I went to day to the Police to change my passport and get one fit to travel with. The business was just the same as before except a small charge of 10 Francs. I did not meet with the person who made out my first passport. He talked a little english but now there was no one who could. Questions however were not very numerous for they proceeded according to the old paper in all that it contained.

---

52   Anne de Bretagne, 1476-1514, twice Queen of France, consort of Charles VIII and of Louis XII. On her death, her heart was placed in her father's tomb in the Church of the Carmelites at Nantes; the tomb was destroyed after the Revolution, and in 1817 re-erected in Nantes Cathedral.

53   A machine for measuring the strength of men or animals, named after the inventor.

S. 19th. This is an important day. The Emperor has just visited the Senate in full state. The weather has been very bad but that did not prevent me and thousands more from going to see the show. I went about 12 o clock to the Tuilleries Gardens & took my station on the Terrace as being the best place then vacant.[54] After waiting some time and getting wet through the trumpet announced the procession. Many guards and many officers of the court passed us before the Emperor came up but at last he appeared in sight. He was sitting in one corner of his carriage covered and almost hidden from sight by an immense robe of ermine and his face overshadowed by a tremendous plume of feathers that descended from a velvet hat. The distance was too great to distinguish the features well but he seemed of a dark countenance and somewhat corpulent - His carriage was very rich and fourteen servants stood upon it in various parts. A numerous guard surrounded him. The Empress and a great number of courtiers &c followed in other carriages. No acclamations were heard where I stood and no comments.

T. 21. I am quite out of patience with the infamous exhorbitance of these Parisians. They seem to have neither sense of honesty nor shame in their dealings. They will ask you twice the value of a thing with as much coolness as if they were going to give it you and when you have offered them half their demand and on their accepting it you reproach them with unfair dealings they tell you "you can afford to pay". It would seem that every tradesman here is a rogue unless they have different meanings for words to what we have.

F. 24. We expect shortly to leave this City and we have no great reason to regret it. It perhaps may be owing partly to the season and partly to my ignorance of the language that I have enjoyed the place so little. The weather has been very bad, very cold much snow rain &c have continually kept the streets in a foul plight. We understand that the winter had set in hard in London but we have no certain information of the state of things there.

M. 27. I was very much amused for half an hour this evening in observing the operations and business of a noted shoe black at the corner of the passage running under the Theatre (Feydeau I think).[55] The shop has two entrances. The interval between is well glazed and preserved in as neat order as the windows of a coffee house along the back of the shop run benches covered with cushions. They are 4 or 5 feet from the ground and a foot board runs at a convenient distance beneath them. When a customer enters he takes his exalted seat and generally a

---

54   The Palace of the Tuileries was Napoleon's residence at the time.
55   Le Théâtre Feydeau, built in 1790 for a troupe of Italian singers. The passage under the theatre was probably la rue des Colonnes.

newspaper (two or three lying constantly in the shop and a spruce shopman immediately makes his feet look the best part about him.[56] The place is well lighted up and the price of all these enjoyments for a soft seat news brilliant boots &c is "what you please".

W. 29. This morning we left Paris[57] after a residence in it of three months and prepared ourselves for new objects and new scenes. The morning was fine but very cold and frosty but on entering the forest of Fontainbleau we did not regret the severity of the weather for I do not think I ever saw a more beautiful scene than that presented to us on the road. A thick mist which had fallen during the night and which had scarcely cleared away had by being frozen dressed every visible object in a garment of wonderful airiness & delicacy. Every small twig and every blade of herbage was encrusted by a spendid coat of hoar frost the crystals of which in most cases extended above half an inch. This circumstance instead of causing a sameness as might have been expected produced an endless variety of shades and forms. Openings in the foreground placed far-removed objects in view which in their airyness and softened by distance appeared as clouds fixed by the hands of an enchanter: then rocks hills valleys streams and roads then a mile stone a cottage or human beings came into the moving landscape and rendered it ever new and delightful. We slept this night at Nemours.

T. 30. Though cold and dark we were on our way to Moulin by 5 o clock this morning and though somewhat more south than London yet I do not perceive any superior character in the winter mornings here. However as we always judge worse of a bad thing when it is present than at any other time I may have been too cross with the cold and dark character of our early hours - The moon had set a circumstance to be regretted for though assisted only by the faintness of star light yet I am sure our road was beautiful 'twas along the bank of the river and within a few yards of the water which indeed at times came to the horses feet. On our left was a series of small hills and valleys lightly wooded and varied now and then by clust'ring habitations - These dark hours however have their pleasures and those are not slight which are furnished at such hours by the memory or the imagination. I have often regretted the interruption caused by the change of horses or the mending of broken harness. 'Tis pleasant to state almost audibly to the mind the novelty of present circumstances that the Loire is on my right hand that the houses to the left contain men of another country to myself that it is french ground I am passing over and then to think of the distance between myself and those who alone feel an interest for me and to enjoy the

---

56   Brackets do not close in manuscript.
57   John Davy, op.cit. p.471, says they left Paris on 23 December, but Faraday's date
      seems more reliable. Davy's poem, 'Fontainebleau', quoted by John Davy, is dated
      'Dec.29, 1813'.

feeling of independence and superiority we at present possess over those sleeping around us. We seem tied to no spot confined by no circumstances at all hours at all seasons and in all places. We move with freedom our world appears extending and our existence enlarged[;] we seem to fly over the globe rather like satellites to it than parts of it and mentally take possession of every spot we go over.

Day appeared and the sun at last arose and now we saw the variety and beauty of the land. It was hilly and indeed mountainous in the distance and as we often had the river in view the scenery was doubly beautiful. As the day advanced all inconvenience from cold vanished and the weather bore the appearance of summer. I saw the sun rise and through the whole of its course in this December day it has not been veiled by the slightest cloud.

After the sun had set about 15 minutes the phenomenon called the Zodiacal light presented itself. It appeared as an emanation of light in enormous rays from the sun into the expanse. There were about seven rays diverging upwards and sideways and ascending many degrees into the heavens. They continued for nearly half an hour without any particular alteration in their appearance but as the quantity of light diminished they became fainter and at last disappeared.

We slept the night at Briare.

F. 31. We have lived hard this last day of the year and have prospects of lying the night as hardly. We arose early travelled hastily fared meagrely and arrived fatigued and at a late hour at Moulins. The latter part of this journey was very delightful being amongst mountains and scenery of the most beautiful kind. As we travelled late we had the advantage of a romantic moonlight to this wild and varied country and the effect produced by the combination of these circumstances was heightened by the covering of snow that enveloped the earth. To lessen as much as possible the labour of the poor tired post horses we alighted and walked for some miles through these wild valleys and passes. There were numberless spots which with the introduction of the carriage and ourselves by this kind of light afforded good subjects for the artist. At last my amusement failed me and notwithstanding all the enchantments of the way I longed for the humbler gratification afforded by a supper and a bed. These were obtained about 10 o clock and welcomed by immediate appropriation.

S. 1. I was saluted on this the morn of the new year by the hostler about 3 o clock with a request to get up. I must confess I never felt more inclined to remain where I was than at that time but as a little inconvenience now would procure accomodation earlier at night I arose took coffee and protecting myself as well as I could from a very cold air was ready to proceed - Of Moulins it can scarcely be supposed that I should know much as we were not in it more than 5 hours and those in the middle of the night. It appeared large and prosperous. There was

much bustle in the Hotel and many respectable townsmen passed in and
out and the accomodations there were such as indicated it the Hotel of
a large place. There were some curious characters at the ordinary[58] but
hunger allowed of no attention but to the appetite and to the goodness
and abundance of the fare.

This day has been very cold but fine. I have slept the greater part
of it and consequently know little of the places we passed - We sleep
tonight I do not know where.

S. 2. We reached Lyons at a very early hour this afternoon and
consequently saw it even at first sight in all its bustle and the
circumstance of the day being Sunday was in this respect somewhat
advantageous to us. After passing through a very long suburb and
attracting all the dirty inhabitants of it to the road side we entered what
is properly the town at a part the farthest removed I believe from the
Hotel we were going to - Hotel du Nord - The town is a busy one and
well peopled that is as far as numbers go. The sight is little capable of
estimating at once their quality but from the number of shops one would
be induced to imagine most of them tradesmen and their consequent
labourers. The rivers Rhone and Saone traverse the city and form a
junction a little distance below it. The situation is singular being very
rocky and the houses stand partly on the rock and partly at their feet.
On the banks of the Saone in the town they rise perpendicularly to a
great height and as you pass along the road which runs immediately
beneath and seems cut out of them the houses above almost threaten to
fall on you. Very fatigued and well pleased with a night's rest.

M. 3. Rambled about the town to day - found many parts of it
much superior to those I had seen yesterday and found that there was
very abundant and excellent accomodation, in the fine streets and places
I now saw, for a race of inhabitants superior to those which before served
to make up the population. There were several English families in the
town as prisoners. Some of them were tradesmen. The men had married
with the townswomen and had gradually settled into citizens not however
absolutely such as the Lyonese themselves make, and they expressed
strong fears that in the present state of things the Government would still
consider them as prisoners and remove them from the town in its present
threatened state to the great injury of their trades and pecuniary affairs.
It was very laughable to hear their account of the transformation of the
inhabitants into guards for the public places and the travels of the only
dozen of muskets in the town through their hands. Perhaps however the
remains of national spirit did in some degree influence them in giving
this description but the town certainly had no means of serious defence
against an enemy.

---

58   A room where a public meal is regularly provided at a fixed price.

The markets appeared lively and in the full progress of business but much of this bustling appearance results from the petty character of the dealers and their great numbers. Every country person sells the article they produce immediately in the market and frequently instead of selling to one great trader employs several deputies[;] a circumstance which multiplies appearances without increasing the actual quantity of business.

The Quays on the banks of the Rhone are very fine and make excellent pleasure walks. The bridges over the river are very good. When the weather is fine which is the case at present I think they must be by far the pleasantest part of the town. I entered by chance into a church of the Patron Saint of the town S^t.[   ].[59] It of course had had extraordinary attention paid to it and was richly ornamented. The short time I remained in it did not permit of a close examination into its various parts. The painted glass was handsome.

The Hotel we are in is a very excellent one and it is but fair that whilst marking down the singular wants of places professing to be for accomodation I notice also such as answer to their professions. The house is large warm and actually comfortable. It perhaps might not have this last point of character in England because of a little dirt a little too much of publicity in the different parts of it and some little privation but standing as it does in a French town it is eminently so. The accomodations particularly with respect to food are excellent good victuals good wine good fruit and plenty of all are great things to travellers and when to these are added a tolerably clean bed and bedroom great inducements to halt a day or two are presented. - Lastly you always have a cheerful obliging host he will answer you any question he says he will do any thing for you and frequently does do things apparently entirely from goodnature and though a suspicion may lurk in the mind that these things are intended to make you content with the bill when you get it yet even the appearance of liberal goodnature is pleasant and <u>will</u> have its effect.

T. 4. After some search I found a road which took me up above on the heights that over hang the town and at last I got to a fine commanding spot. This however was not without transgressing on holy ground for I had to scale the wall of a church yard that was situated on the brow of a cliff and make use of the railing for a seat. From hence I saw a great extent of country on the south and south east side of the city and a large part of the city itself. The panoramic view presented was very beautiful. The Rhone coming down from the country passed by the town and glided below & before me. The regularity of that part of the town which came under view extended to some distances and then from among it on the right hand the Saone appeared and at a little

---

59   St Jean.

distance joined the Rhone increasing its already large stream nearly twofold. Boats some large and some small were moving on the river and also a few rafts and these objects with curling smoke here and there and a very fine sky made a beautiful picture.

On returning home I had the luck of seeing the Senator from Paris enter the town. It seems the Emperor has dispatched all the Senators to their respective departments and this had just arrived at his department. Placards were immediately stuck up about the town calling the inhabitants to arms and exhorting them to resist the approaching enemy. Both arms and soldiers are however very scarce and it is probable that the words of this town will surpass the feats.

I understand there are boats of passage which descend the river from this place to Avignon and I imagine it is possible we shall go by one of them - shall see to night.

W. 5. Left Lyons this morning with Post horses at the moderate hour of 9 o clock and took our route by the side of the Rhone towards Avignon. To day many new and interesting objects appeared and nature put on much grander forms than she had before shewn us. The Rhone rolled along on our right hand and on her opposite shore a range of mountains appeared the tops of which were often hidden in clouds and when that veil rolled off they displayed summits of snow. On the left hand in the distance the Alps arose stretching out one chain beyond another. The Dauphiny Alps were about 60 miles from us and the farthest range full 100 miles off. The unclouded sun illuminated their white summits and the clear sky allowed them to be seen as if but a few miles distant. Mont Blanc was readily distinguished. It appeared as an enormous isolated[?] mass of white rocks. At sun set as the light decreased their summits took a hundred varying hues. The tone of colouring changed rapidly as the luminary sank down became more grave at last appeared of a dull red as if ignited and then disappeared in the obscurity until fancy and the moon again faintly made them visible - Slept at Valence?

T. 6. Continued to track the banks of the Rhone and enjoy the country &c &c. At moonlight crossed the Rhone by the Pont d'Esprit an enormous bridge for length but I confess I was too sleepy to notice it. We slept at a village on the western side of the Rhone.

F. 7 To day we passed two fine pieces of old Roman Architecture. Our way to Montpellier took us across the river Gardon by the bridge called Pont du Gard. At this place is an old aqueduct in almost a perfect state at least it appeared so during the transient and passing view we had of it. It was constructed of large blocks of stone very few of which seemed to have left their places. It had three tiers of arches. The lowest and largest were six in number through which the river passed. The second tier eleven and the third tier thirty eight at present but some seem to have fallen into decay and disappeared at each end. Its position is directly across the river and it connects the high banks on each side. It is supposed to have been created by Agrippa when he came into Languedoc about 19 years before the birth of our Saviour to conduct the waters of the fountains Eure and Airan to Nismes.[60] The whole height is 150 feet. The lowest tier of arches is 531 feet in length and the principal arch which admits the strain is 83 feet in width. The second tier of arches is 64 feet high and 850 feet in length. The third is 25½ feet high and 868 feet in length. Immediately above it is the water-way. This aqueduct is between Remoulins and Nismes about 4 leagues from the latter place.

A modern bridge of stone has been attached to the side of this aqueduct for the convenience of crossing the river. The arches are made to correspond with those of the aqueduct and the appearance of this side at a distance is not altered except in the freshness of the work: on the other side it is not altered at all.

About two hours after we passed through Nismes renowned for its ampitheatre[61] our road lay close to it and the carriage was stopped for a few minutes to allow a momentary glimpse. It is considered perhaps as the finest building of the kind next to Vespasians at Rome. It is of an elliptical form. The largest diameter 456 feet and the shortest 332 feet. Its height is 66 feet. It is built in the Tuscan order though irregular and approaching the Doric. It originally contained 32 ranges of seats of which 17 remain at present. There are three ranges of vomitories or doors for the admission and departure of the people. By allowing 20 inches for each person it is calculated that the building would contain 17000 persons.

Though it is as yet early in the year the plants and trees have in many places budded and the olive trees which are now abundant preserve a constant verdure. This with the serenity of the atmosphere and a bright sun makes the country seem in a constant smile but the inhabitants complain of the hard winter and fear it will even be worse.

S. 8. Reached Montpellier to day at a very good hour about 2 o clock. The weather has been very cold and frosty all the morning more so I think than at any time before this winter but the sky is beautifully clear and brilliant. We have passed many olive plantations and are now in a country famous for fine oil. I believe we shall remain here some time and have opportunity to notice the country. The town seems to be very pretty but the Hotel we are in must not be compared to that at Lyons except for good oil and wine and goodnature in all the persons in it.

---

60   Now Nîmes.
61   amphitheatre.

S. 9. Took a couple of strolls about the town to facilitate longer walks. The place is moderate in size and irregular in its form and internal construction but with very pleasant outskirts and very pretty promenades. The streets are generally narrow and irregular and many of them hilly. A few fountains here & there do not so much serve the purposes of ornament as of utility. The church is situated in the lowest part of the town so that above half of it is below the level of the greater number of houses. - There seems an astonishing number of booksellers in town for so small a place.

M. 10. Stretched my legs on the place du Peyrou the ornament and pride of Montpellier. I had heard much of it but though my expectations were raised they were not disappointed a circumstance attributable to their being formed on the character and size of the town as much as on the reports I heard of the beauty grandeur &c of the Peyrou. - It is a vast terrace raised 28 or 30 feet above the level of the surrounding soil which itself is the highest part in or near the town. It stands north of the town and the entrance on to it is opposite the town gate. It is ornamented with walks trees fountains &c and a beautiful little temple which terminates an aqueduct supplying the terrace and the town with water. Even at this period of the year the place is highly agreeable and is the general resort of the inhabitants in the sunny afternoons of the fine but wintry days.

The aqueduct which joins the temple at the opposite end of the Peyrou to the entrance is of modern workmanship. It was built about 70 years ago and brings the waters of the fine fountain of St Clement to the Peyrou where after being ornamental in a high degree they are distributed to various parts of the town and supply the fountains. The structure has two tiers of arches the number in the lower being 51 in the upper 183. Each lower arch is surmounted by three upper ones and the remainder repose on the side of the hill of St Clement's spring. From the spring to the commencement of the lower arch was 140 full steps[;] each lower arch with a pier took more than 12 steps making in the whole for the arches 612 paces and there were 40 more on the terrace. The whole number therefore is 792 and I should think the aqueduct to be more than 800 yards in length. By comparing its height with imaginary marks in the base which I afterwards paced I suppose it to be 30 yard where the ground sank lowest. The fountain of St Clement is directly north of the Peyrou so that the aqueduct stretches out into the country from the terrace and forms a fine object in the landscape. The water is very pure and abundant. They are first delivered from the sculptured rocky base of the temple into a basin stored with fish and then run off by pipes to the different parts of the town.

T. 11. Took a long walk to Mont Ferrier an extinct volcano distant to the N E about four miles. The country itself is limestone but varied in a singular way by the occurrence of this hill and basalt at a little distance from it. The hill is conical and has just the appearance of an extinct volcano it is barren and its surface covered with decomposing scoria and small fragments of volcanic production. No doubt can exist as to its having at some time been a very active volcano. - The place where the basalt occurs is at a village about two miles off. The village stands on a hill of basalt and at the summit the naked rock is seen coming up from under the soil - Mont Ferrier is a proof of the existence of igneous agents in this country at one time and the plutonians[62] will adduce the existence of basalt as a further evidence of this fact.

The verdure of the country round Montpellier is very pleasant. This is not exactly the time of year in which to remark it nor is the ground that we have passed over the very best for that purpose at any time but there are two things which will justify me as far as I mean to proceed. These are the olives and the pines. The olive tree is of small size rarely larger than a cherry tree frequently much smaller. Its form is generally pretty being irregular and broken into parts by the formation of large branches at a little distance from the root. The leaf is small and uniform in its appearance and of a pale dull green. At hand the tint is not a pleasant one but distance and the absence of almost all other greens render it very acceptable and when mingled with the fine deep hue of the pine produces an effect of a very superior kind - The pines are short but airy. The straight extension of their arms and the light mobile character of their foliage added to the different colours assumed at different ages render them extremely fit to mingle with the olive and in consequence the country may boast of a beautiful verdure in the midst of winter.

F. 14. I have now rambled almost over the whole of this town and begin to think my first character of it not quite good enough. Even under the evil influence of bad weather it has appeared to improve on me. It is situated on inclined ground and some of the streets towards the lower part of it are narrow and steep but in general they are wide open and airy and contain good houses. The shops are pretty and many well furnished and kept. The markets seem busy places, the coffee houses well frequented. The inhabitants are respectable and I have found them very goodnatured and obliging - The weather alone is what we did not expect it to be.

S. 15. Bread wine and water are three things very good and very cheap here. Of bread there are many varieties. What they call pain d'ammunition[63] looks more like brick than bread the price is almost nothing and for that reason much of it is eaten (for the poor people are very poor here). The better sorts of bread are very good and the best is

---

62   Adherents of the geological theory, then fairly new, that attributed most geological phenomena to the action of the earth's internal heat.

63   Pain de munition: a coarse brown bread baked for the army.

more like cake than bread. I think the character the french bread has of surpassing that of most other nations must be well founded. It has a degree of positive excellence that one would not wish it surpassed; beyond what it is would be undue luxury. The wine is that of the country and is cheap because there is no market for it except amongst the inhabitants. It is generally red and very strong. A little of it (Vin de S^t. George) bottle not included does not cost at the first hand more than three pence english and sometimes not nearly so much and there is a wine still more common that sells for much less. - The water is excellent and plentiful but it is not so with the wood and that being the only fuel here it gives rise to much inconvenience or expense this severe winter. The country around being open and uncovered is very scantily productive of this article and it of course becomes very dear. In illustration I may observe that in the hotel where we yet remain it is served out by weight to the inmates a packet is 50 lb and costs 30 sous.

M. 17. The Esplanade is a handsome place (ranking next after the Peyrou) on the Southwest side of the town. It is a terrace raised on the side of the hill on which Montpellier stands level with the highest parts of the town. The length of it is very considerable I should think more than 300 feet and it is perhaps one third of that in width. It is intersected by walks extending along and across it which lead to different points from whence exquisite views of the surrounding country is obtained. The sides of these walks are ornamented with trees and in the middle of the place [?] ostensibly placed as an embellishment but really intended to produce a political effect is a pillar surmounted by the Emperor's Eagle and the letter N both finely gilt and when glittering in the sun capable of being seen at a great distance. On that side of the Esplanade furthest from the town stands the fort a place of considerable size great strength and having the town completely in its power. I entered it and after winding along some dark passages came out into the open space within. The stroll round the ramparts was pleasant but I imagine that at times whilst enjoying myself I was transgressing for the sentinals regarded me sharply and more particularly at least I thought so as I stood looking at one corner where from some cause or other the fortifications were injured. I finished my walk however without personal interruption and was not sorry for it as I had opportunities of seeing the distant country from higher points and better situations than from the esplanade itself. There were houses within and some soldiers but not many a small number must be sufficient to defend this place but I cannot imagine that in this part of the country they will ever have occasion for it. I know nothing of these things but from the situation of Montpellier I suppose it would be useful only if the Spaniards were ever to prove so risen from their lethargy as to enter France. They were firing cannon in the fort I do not know what for nor could our host tell me.

<u>W. 19th</u> It is astonishing to remark the readiness of the French in supplying expedients by which accidental or sudden wants may be satisfied or desired ends obtained and it happens that though these expedients are often awkward inapplicable and even dangerous yet they frequently answer the desired purpose. It is at the same time but fair to say in honor of previous generations that many of these wants and expedients have descended from father to son for several races and consequently that all the merit attached to the means of obviating them is not due to the present race but belongs in part at least to their progenitors[;] as for instance horses have been tied together by ropes for the want of harness for I dare say this hundred years and therefore the merit of supplying straps by ropes, buckles by knots, saddles by wisps of straw, whips by words, and stirrups by nothing belong properly to the ancestors of the present race and they of course ought to have their due share of praise[;] at the same time every day proves that their sons continue to improve on this practice and that they will in this happy country shortly bring it to perfection.

These thoughts arise by that slender kind of association which can only be traced without the appearance of absurdity by the thinker himself from having this morning seen considerable packages weighed very readily in the market place by the steelyard which instrument appears to be in considerable use here. The extremities of a pole were placed on the shoulders of two men and a steelyard attached to the middle of it. Instantly bags baskets &c were hung on the hooks weighed quickly and taken away and in two minutes the same men were repeating their work in another part of the market. - I have not the least fault to find with this method of weighing but I think we may trace its origin to the habit they seem to be in here of supplying things by expedients. As all the market folk must at times want to weigh goods both in large and small quantities the mode of meeting their wants would be to have each his instruments to weigh with. It seems however that when the market was begun each had not his own scales but that an odd pair or a steelyard was borrowed which circulating through the market continues to do so 'till the present day.

As an instance of their dangerous expedients I will describe their manner of sawing large pieces of timber. I do not know that it is the only method but it is a way I have often seen adopted. They have a kind of stool with three legs two of which are about 6 feet long and the third 16 or 18. The upper end of the long leg is continued for a short distance beyond the insertion of the other legs and to this part the piece of wood to be sawn is affixed. The piece is sometimes 6 feet in length and a foot in thickness and must weigh some hundred weight the manner of attaching it to the projecting end of the long leg is to lay it upon the end overlapping 8 or 10 inches and binding both about once or twice with a chain. A considerable weight is then laid on the end of the long leg which acting as a lever preserves the beam in an elevated horizontal position. When thus arranged one man will mount on the log whilst

another stands under it and commence[s] sawing at the farthest extremity. In this state of things should a link of the chain give way and there must be a force of some tons on it at times or the weight at the extremity of the long leg slips it is scarcely possible to conceive how the under man should escape being killed and the upper one serious injury.

For another instance I will point out their jack boots weighing from 14 lb upwards each – These are wadded padded and stuffed with wool rags and hay and all (I give their own reason) to preserve their legs from being hurt should the carriage be overturned[;] an amusing contingency for the traveller to be reminded of.

F. 21. I went this evening to the theatre it was small but very pretty. As I know but little French and they pronounce it here with a very provincial accent it was scarcely possible I should understand what the actors said. I did not expect it but I unexpectedly found out the meaning by that universal language gesture for it was most exuberantly employed. The audience seemed highly delighted with the acting & actor the latter was a great favourite. The theatre closed at an early hour.

S. 22. The fountains except that on the Peyrou are not handsome but there are several which from their antiquated form and old gothic ornaments have a curious appearance and their oddness would make one regret their removal. They are not numerous in the lower parts of the town and a circumstance which adds to their importance as fountains is the increased force they gain in those low situations from the superior height of the head of water. During a late frosty fit their appearance underwent considerable changes from the formation of enormous icicles which connecting various parts together before separated and giving a peculiar and airy drapery where before was none seemed to have replaced the old fountains by new ones. I have felt much pleasure during a few night strolls about the town in viewing the fountains in this state but the pleasure was heightened by other circumstances. Although frosty very little snow has yet fallen so that the streets are very clean and dry. The nights are generally clear & serene. The moon has shone bright and the inhabitants have been housed. In this state I find a town very interesting[;] you see the latest possible marks of human beings you see every thing constructed for their use and convenience but you see none of the persons themselves and may easily imagine them far away. It is indeed the best possible situation for the mind to abstract man from the artificial supplies which he obtains for his wants equally artificial and to consider them independant of each other.

S. 23. I am almost deterred from learning the French language for here we have scarcely any use for it. The language of the country is a disagreeable patois and there are many who cannot talk French at all many also do so but very provincially. Books are almost universally printed in French language. There however exist some in the Patois itself and a book of poems in that language are much praised by the author of a description of Montpellier. This Patois seems difficult to learn and I do not believe that a grammar of it exists.

M. 24. In passing through the market this morning I stopped for a few minutes to look at the stall, booth or whatever else it might be called of a religious pedler. He had entered the market with a large box on his back similar to a London puppet show. This was soon placed upright on two stools and when the folding doors were opened displayed to the surrounding attentive multitude a vast number of beads crucifixes crosses &c &c of various sizes. Four poles were then erected behind the repository and three large rough paintings on paper representing the crucifixion &c suspended from them and now the man and his wife being mounted on stools began to chaunt & soon produced a marvellous effect on the crowd money came in rapidly and their stock of rosaries &c was soon much diminished. When I left them the same lucrative trade was going on with undiminished vigour. I have no doubt but that that man has made more money today than any other person in the market.

W. 26 I took a hasty walk to day round the Jardin des Plantes. I understand it is extremely well arranged in all its parts.

F. 28. Visited the Booksellers shops, the books principally Parisian and stereotyped. There is only one printer and one bookbinder in the town. Little of Novelty appears here except accounts of wonderful cures.

S. 29. We have had no reason as yet to form a favourable idea of the climate of Montpellier, that climate which when united to the medical abilities of the faculty no disease can withstand. As yet the weather continues cold though finer than it has been. The inhabitants consider the season as extremely severe. A sharp frost prevailed for the last few days but a thaw commenced yesterday and some snow fell. We have had much rain and very disagreeable weather. The winter has not been so sharp for the last three years and many persons declare that so much snow has not fallen in one season for the last twenty years. The frost is I understand very sharp at Paris and renders the streets almost impassable to carriages. - How the season the friends and their circumstances are in London is an enquiry often mentally made but it still returns on the mind with regret as it still remains unanswered.

M. 31. By an early walk to the Peyrou this morning I enjoyed the fine scene of sun rise and a clear unsullied view of the beautiful and extensive landscape. From this spot I could see around me the Alps the Pyrenees the Mediterranean and the town as well as the country in the near neighbourhood at the moment the sun first illuminated them.

The aqueduct walls and other parts of the masonry of the Peyrou are built with a stone astonishingly filled with organic remains indeed one fourth part of the materials may be considered as shells these are of various kinds though principally bivalves resembling small cockle shells. This stone is obtained from [   ] a place not very distant from Montpellier about 4 or 5 leagues.

T. 1. This morning the town was all in an uproar and running to see the passing of a large train of artillery which is going up towards Lyons. They seem in great haste.

W. 2. Since we have been here Sir Humphry has continued to work very closely on iodine. He has been searching for it in several of the plants that grow in the Mediterranean but has not obtained certain evidences of its presence. If it exists in them at all it is in very minute quantities and it will be scarcely possible to detect it.

T. 3. A walk this morning beyond the fortifications took me by a very pleasant path amongst the olives and vines but they are doing nothing with them now except a chance man or two who cut off the long shoots of the vines to make up into faggots or what they call sarments. The vineyards have a very bare uninteresting appearance in winter. The trees are set in the ground in rows about 18 inches or 2 feet apart and are not trained upon trellises but after they are clipped and pruned an operation that will soon commence here sticks about a yard long are stuck in the ground one to each root and the shoots tied to it. The husbandmen are very careful in hoeing and clearing the ground and the vines seem to require more attention than any thing else they cultivate.

The olive trees require no care except that of dunging their roots every two or three years and of gathering the fruit when ripe. I have noticed in many of them where rents or breaks in the tree occur as where an arm has come off or the trunk has split that they are careful every now and then to cut away the old surface and lay the sound heart wood bare and sometimes when the trunk has a very irregular form it appears as if the whole of one side had been planed. I have as yet seen scarcely a single berry on the trees but to make amends we have them constantly at table.

S. 5. Drilling is now the occupation of the town and the Peyrou looks like a Parade. During the morning it is covered by clusters of clumsy recruits who are endeavouring to hold their arms right, turn their toes out, keep their hands in, hold their hands up &c according to the direction of certain corporals who are at present all authority and importance.

S. 6. The pope passed through this place a few days ago in his way to Italy he has just been set at liberty.[64] The good catholics here have in expectation of his coming been talking of his sufferings and trouble for many days past and at every hour felt their curiosity and devotion rise higher at last he came not to stop in the town as was supposed but merely to pass by the outside of it. Early in the morning the road was well peopled and before 10 o clock almost every person in the town was there but myself. They say he was received in a very pathetic manner and with a multitude of sighs tears and groans. Some people accompanied him for miles from the town and some had in the morning gone many miles to meet him.

M. 7. Left Montpellier this morning with fine frosty weather and after a while a beautiful sunrise. To day we retrod the ground we had before passed over and drove on to Nismes. The landscape was beautiful and rendered active by the presence of the industrious neighbour. The principal vegetation was of olive trees but the vines now had their attention. Men were busy pruning them and cutting off the long runners of last year and women were employed in tying them up into parcels for fuel. In some parts they were dunging the olive trees and some of the largest had been cut down. This was more because of their size than for any other reason for a large tree is not so valuable in proportion to its size as a small one. It is necessary at the gathering season that the fruit should be plucked by the hand the oil being injured in its quality by the least bruise in it but to get it from the high boughs they are obliged to beat it down with poles and then the very thing they wish to avoid is according to their process inevitable.

We arrived at Nismes about 12 o clk and devoted the rest of the day to a view of the antiquities and remains of Roman grandeur and luxury that are to be found here.

---

64   Pius VII (Pope, 1800-1823) had been deported to France in July 1809 following the annexation of the Papal States by Napoleon.

After dinner I walked out and proceeded first to the "Arean"[65] or Ampitheatre which I have already noticed. In former times the whole of the lower external part of the building was but a series of entrances but iron railing has been placed in these arches and one passage only has been left open and this assists considerably in preserving it from the mischievous hands of the idle and unemployed. Entering at the open arch I passed into an arcade or gallery that ran round the building; from this gallery entrances formerly conducted the people to the lower seats but at present they conduct to ruins, the lower tier of seats having fallen in. Stairs led from these passages to an upper gallery similar to and situated over the lower one and from this entrance gave admission to the middle tiers of seats and stairs afforded means of mounting to the third and smallest gallery which last conducted to the top seats or which is the same thing to the top of the building. At present access is easily gained to the lower end by climbing over rubbish to the second gallery but I found no very easy ascent to the top though I am told there is one tolerably commodious. I however reached it. The floors of the galleries particularly the second are very irregular and uneven in places sometimes rising into elevations of 6 or 8 inches caused by the changing and destroying influence of time or by accidents being evidently owing to the disjunction of the stones. All the parts of the building that are yet standing seem as if they would stand for ever. The stones are very large and the joints in general firm and close. The upper seats have suffered the least and are so perfect that a person may pass around seven eighths of the ampitheatre on one seat. They are arranged as a flight of steps the upper seat or step being the summit of the building. The breadth and fall of each is about 20 or 22 inches. There were formerly 32 ranges of seats and I counted 16 remaining in the most perfect part.

In the lower part and beneath the lowest seats are the dens and caves in which the beasts were confined and various galleries and passages still exist there. A large port or entrance exists at each end of the long diameter of the ampitheatre for the admission of the larger beasts and for the triumphal exit of the victor in the games: at present they are useful for the admission of carts which are employed to carry out the earth that encumbers the lower part of the building. Many men are employed in clearing the passages and cells in order to render it a fit place for amusement and to shew more distinctly this fine specimen of antiquity. - I have said to render it fit for amusement and I am told that even in its present state it is often employed for that purpose in the summer season when on Sunday evenings men & beasts collect here though not as in former times and the whole ampitheatre is filled with coursing, wrestling, running &c.

In one part which is easily accessible there are on the wall five sculptured heads of Roman Emperors. They are accompanied by

---

65   Les Arenes, the Roman amphitheatre constructed at the end of the first century BC.

inscriptions but the whole is much injured by time. They were formerly situated in the middle gallery but are now exposed to the weather by the ruin and falling away of that part of the building.

At one place on the top of the building circumstances were very favourable to view at least the appearance of the cement[;] its hardness equalled that of the stone and it adhered to it as if it were a part of it but a small quantity appeared to be in the joints. From its colour and appearance one would suppose it to contain much iron.

Leaving the Ampitheatre I went to the Grand Fountain and in going to it passed the building called La Maison Quarrée.[66] It is considered a beautiful specimen of antient Architecture is of the corinthian order and was built about the year 754 of Rome by the people of Nismes in honor of Caius and Lucius the sons of Agrippa. The inscription by which the information is given has been made out in a very ingenious manner by the marks of the nails with which the bronze letters were formerly attached to the Frieze. - I was told that 'till about 18 years ago it was used as a church but at present it is shut up. There are some large mosaic pavements in it.

The Grande Fountain is a work admirably suited to give the mind correct ideas of Roman magnificence and luxury. It is not in its present state a relic of former things because having been rebuilt or at least the parts that were destroyed replaced modern workmanship interferes but from the situation and design alone of the fountain and gardens enough may be gathered to inform us that their refinement and elegance in this kind of ornament and enjoyment was as high as it well could be. This place is also interesting in no small degree from the peculiar situation and magnitude of the springs. Rocks of enormous magnitude and height are so thrown together by nature as to form a broken kind of crescent. Here the fountain or river rises a small smooth lake appears in which various water plants are luxuriently growing: from this lake a strong and copious stream of water issues or rather two streams for it is divided in passing under gardens and walks which are supported on pillars; from hence it is conducted into a square basin in the middle of which is a small and beautiful flower garden here it divides again and branches off circulating in fine[?] canals through the general gardens which are of considerable size and prettily laid out and ornamented with shrubs and flowers but this is not the best season to find them in their beauty. These canals unite at the end of the garden and flow in a strong clear stream into the town. In its course through the town it passes over two dams of masonry forming handsome cascades and is crossed in previous parts by several elegant bridges. When the stream has quitted the gardens & is not more than 200 yards from its source it is full 18 feet wide and two deep and moves very quickly. Inscriptions are fixed in the rocks at the fountain

---

66   La Maison Carrée, a Roman temple in the Greek style built in the first century BC.

head in two similar and appropriate places but they have long been illegible.

This place was by the various and overwhelming accidents of time nearly buried and forgotten. The canal was filled up with earth and the springs stopped or diverted. It is not more than a century ago that the encumbring rubbish was cleared away and the broken or destroyed parts rebuilt but this has been done in a manner approaching to the antient style and thus an adequate idea may be formed of what it originally was.

On the top of the Rock above the fountain are the ruins of an old Tower called Tour Magne. It also was built by the Romans and is supposed to have been a Pharos. I did not go up to it.

In the gardens are the remains of a Roman edifice called at present The temple of Diana. The interior is now very plain indeed what is seen is principally modern work for part of the walls and roof having given way a slight stone wall has been raised merely to close the opening and preserve what remains from dispoiling hands. I entered the temple of a goddess who as my guide observed had more admirers in former days than at present and looked into the various niches and recesses. Opposite to the door was a large niche and altar where the goddess according to modern accounts was worshipped. On each side were two smaller niches which were continued upwards as a pipe and here the oracle uttered its ambiguous disclosing concealing sentences. On the right hand by the oracle was an entrance which took us into a smaller place cutt off from the body of the temple by a wall and here (said my guide) the beasts were slaughtered. The whole building appears to have been erected without cement: in several places the joints may be seen through and in other parts there is no appearance of any connecting substance in them. The roof has been arched; but two thirds or perhaps three fourths have fallen in, the rest remaining in its original position. The stone ceiling is handsomely sculptured over the recesses in flowers and branches and this work is very perfect. The pillars that support the recesses are square and each of one piece.

There are several fragments of Roman sculpture and inscriptions in the body of the temple some of which belong to the place and others have been found in the town, for all that from time to time are discovered are deposited here. There are some very perfect & beautiful friezes &c.

Nismes also contains some fine pieces of mosaic pavement. These are to be found in the houses of three private persons.

T. 8. Left Nismes and a goodnatured Landlord who talked broken english at 6 o clock and proceeded on our way with fine weather. After a while the sun rose majestically promising us a clear unclouded day. Olives and vines were the objects in the fore ground and in the back of the landscape. Mont Ventoux with its summit cloathed with snow and clouds filled up the scene. With this mountain the Alps commence and it is no mean indication of their grandure & magnitude.

In a few hours we recrossed the Pont du Gard. With regard to the aqueduct it may be observed that the stones in the upper part of the middle tier of arches are corroded in a singular manner. Cavities of an imperfect wedge like form being produced by the dissolving power of water which though weak yet when thus continued for a length of time produces striking effects.

From hence we passed on to Avignon and in our approach to the town crossed two arms of the Rhone the first of them in a boat. For this purpose a rough platform which runs a yard or two into the river is erected on the shore and is level with the boat which lays alongside of it. The carriage is thus easily placed across the boat the horses being taken from it and placed in one end. A rope of great strength is stretched across the river, being elevated at each end on two poles and on this another rope runs by a pully attached to one end of it, the other being fastened to the vessel. When all is ready the boat is unmoored and the stream of the river aided by a proper use of the rudder carries it across to a platform similar to the first erected on the opposite shore.

The city and neighbouring country had a very fine appearance as we approached it. The old palace of the Popes (in former times) appearing in the view. After crossing another arm of the Rhone by a bridge we entered the town but did not stop there more than three hours for hiring three horses for a few days[;] we passed on by bye roads to Lisle[67] near to Vauclause in order to see the famous fountain of that place[68] and the abode of Petrarch. Slept at Lisle.

<u>W. 9.</u> We prepared this morning to go to the fountains which are about 2 or 3 miles from the Inn we slept at and at 10 o clock were on the road. As we approached the rock which seemed to rise like a barrier before us a beautiful river appeared coming from the spot we were going to when still nearer the ruins of a Chateau came in view, the Chateau of Petrarch and at last the whole scene opened out before us and the mountains and rocks which stopped our course presented a view in itself sufficient for that purpose - We left the carriage in a little village at a short distance from the source of the river and proceeded on foot to the base of the rock where the tortuous valley through which our road lay was suddenly closed by the perpendicular sides of limestone mountains of enormous height. Beneath the brow of a rock at the very extremity of the valley appeared a small still lake and in the middle of it a pillar erected A PETRARQUE The water precipitates from this lake over enormous rocks and dashing in between them through a fall of many feet produces a sea of foam which still as it advances overcomes the opposing barriers till it gains the plains. In various parts the water rises out from

---

67   L'Isle-sur-la-Sorgue.
68   La Fontaine de Vaucluse. The Italian poet, Petrarch (Francesco Petrarca, 1304-
       1374) lived here, but not in the castle, 1337 to 1353.

between the rocks in smaller streams or forcing upwards through the pebbles joins the great mass already irresistable.

At some little distance from the head and after having passed two or three beautiful cascades the stream divides into branches forming three rivers of considerable size. The water is extremely clear and pure and of a beautiful green colour. The bed of the river is carpetted with a thousand water plants and an eternal verdure seems to reign in the environs of Petrarchs haunts. Even the limestone rocks were in some places ornamented by olives and vines and at their summmits were cloathed with thyme and other odoriferous herbs. Juniper Ilexs and box trees were abundant.

On approaching the end of the valley and the source of the river a wind of some strength is felt as proceeding from the rock. This Sir H Davy said he supposed to come partly from the ground and to be partly caused by the rapid motion of so large a body of water.

The mountains are limestone of which the strata incline variously veins of flint run through the rock in many places cutting the strata in different angles. Small spiral univalves are very abundant.

Sir H Davy said he was inclined to attribute the origin of this river to the melting of the snow on Mont Ventoux (which had been a prominent object in view during yesterdays journey). Its situation favours this idea - it being off from the head of the river 8 or 10 miles: and that it originates from that or a similar cause is also probable from the fluctuation it suffers at different seasons. The two most proper times of visiting it are the spring and autumnal equinoxes[;] at the spring equinox it is in its full force and beauty, at the autumnal equinox it is lowest and the cavern from which it issues is only at that time capable of being examined.

T. 10. Left Lisle this morning and advanced again towards the post road and to Aix. The environs of Lisle are rendered beautiful by the meanderings of the river of Vauclouse. We soon came on to ground which was nothing but soft sand and gravel. This tract extended to a great distance on each side of the river Durance and marked the extent of its ravages when extraordinarily filled by rapid thaws or heavy rains. We crossed the river in a boat and soon reached the great road.

After sunset I again saw the Zodiacal light in great perfection. The phenomenon appeared about 30' after the sun was set and continued perhaps for 30' more. The rays were exceedingly clear and distinct. They were much stronger in the lower part of the horizon than at an elevation of 20° or 30° and extended more than twice as far on each side of the sun in an inclined direction as they did upwards in a vertical direction perhaps in some way or other they may have a dependance on or relation to the atmosphere or to particular states of it. The rays appeared to extend much farther in a southern than in a northern direction the luminary of course being westward. We reached Aix about 6 o clock.

F. 11   To day took a walk round Aix and the environs.   The
weather is warm and beautiful, vegetation is fast advancing every thing
seems cheerful and summer on the verge of coming. I found many small
green lizards basking on a bank of lettuces in the rays of the sun. They
were too nimble to be caught.

S. 12. Aix like the other towns of France is watered by Fountains
and wells but the singularity attends some of them of being supplied by
hot springs for which and for its baths this town is well known. In the
great street of Aix at one end of which our Hotel is situated there are
three fountains and the middle and largest one is supplied by a hot
spring. This morning a slight frost had chilled the air and the vapour of
the water was visible ascending to a great height forming a curious and
picturesque effect. I found its temperature to be 80° F. and that of one
of the others 50° F. The third I did not try by a thermometer but it felt
of a common temperature. The springs do not rise immediately under the
fountain but at some distance and the temperature is much diminished by
the length of pipe it passes through - Behind our Hotel is a place erected
for the use of the Blanchisseurs where the waters of a warm spring are
received into small inclosures at which the women wash.   The
temperature was about 65° F or 68° F.

S. 13 Left Aix this morning. Nothing particular the whole day
for pretty scenery has now become common though not less interesting.
We stopped this evening at an Inn or Auberge where the Pope had
stopped and slept about 6 days ago and this circumstance was not the
least argument the master urged to induce us to stay and at last to make
quite sure of his customers he promised the bed in which his Holiness
had slept.

M. 14. Our rout to day was extremely beautiful and interesting it
lay over fine mountains whose porphyritic rocks rose and diversified the
sides of the roads. The steep sides of the mountains were cloathed with
noble pines which tree here presents a beautiful appearance. Its fine
form, spreading arms and dark green foliage render it one of the most
ornamental trees that can be introduced into a landscape. In the course
of the day the Alps appeared very grand in the distance.
As evening approached we gained upon Frejus and stopped there
for the night. The remains of several roman edifices still exist in the
town. Near the gate are the ruins of an ampitheatre apparently of a
circular form and the town is even now inclosed in some parts by the
antient walls. These and other ruins are of brick not similar to modern
brick work for the antient bricks are more like large tiles and have a
closer grain than ours and are more compact and solid.

T.15. We left Frejus with very cold weather but sun rise soon made it agreeable. The scenery very beautiful on our right hand we had the sea and on our left a long track of ruins formerly part of an aqueduct but at present shewing nothing but ivy bound piers. These were also of brick. We passed over several mountains of porphyry in some places the rock was perfectly hard and solid in others it was decomposing and falling to pieces.

An alarm of robbers was given to us among these mountains by a person whom we met on horseback and who said they had taken from him his portmanteau but nothing turned up which could add to the variety of a journal.

In the afternoon we passed on the road a small pillar about two feet high erected at one of the extremities of the arc of the meridian measured by the French Astronomers, on it was inscribed the words ZONE KILOM^{que}.

A short time afterwards we crossed the river Var over a very long wooden bridge. This being a mountain river is at times astonishingly filled and then sweeps with irresistable force over a wide space at other times as at present it runs in two or three small streams over its immense gravelly bed not covering the fiftieth part of its surface. Some years ago this formed the natural boundary between France and Italy but since the conjunction of the kingdoms this long bridge has been thrown over to facilitate the communication.

The cultivation of the country and the appearance of things are very different on the two sides of the Var. Now the houses are painted and ornamented externally, the dress of the people has changed, the gardens glow with oranges and lemons which stand in forests and the vines creep to the tops of the highest trees. Ornamented in this manner the road to Nice was delightful and it was singularly contrasted by a high coun[t]ry rising before us on the borders of Piedmont and Savoy its top covered with constant snow. - We stopped at the delightful town of Nice.

W. 16. To day we remain at Nice. - I found out the Terrace on the sea shore and had a very pleasant stroll there. The rope maker and the laundress were very busy on the sands the one making his twists and the other bleaching her linen. They have no tide here to interrupt them. But the most striking feature in this country is the orange and lemon trees. The orange tree possesses a very pretty form and appearance and when loaded as at present with the golden fruit is delightful. The lemon tree has more the form of a shrub its trunk is not so strong and its branches more like slips. They have a resemblance to those of the willow its foliage also as well as the fruit is paler in colour than the orange tree which occasions it to have an inferior appearance but both give a striking and forcible idea of a happy climate. The vines are here cultivated in a manner very different to that adopted on the other side of the Var: they are in general planted by the side of other trees as the willow &c and the shoots are wound round the supporting arms of its neighbour: the trunk here ascends to a considerable height sometimes 12 or 14 feet and appears from its contorted form more like a moving snake than a fixed vegetable sometimes they are planted irregularly by the side of the road or in the hedges or in other parts as convenience may permit at other times they are put in double rows and the intervals between differently cultivated.

They have had very little cold weather here this winter we have sat enjoying ourselves at our meals without a fire and with all the doors and windows open so genial & mild is the weather here.

T. 17. Left Nice this morning and advanced towards the Alps by a road on the sides of which were gardens with oranges and lemons in great profusion. We soon entered among the mountains they were of limestone stratified very regularly and appearing at a distance like stairs. At some distance up we came to a place where the strata for many yards consisted of small pieces of limestone an inch in size more or less cemented together by carbonate of lime. Varieties occurred here and there and in these places the cement had taken a stalactitic form. - A dropping well added to the variety of objects and appearing in a very picturesque situation added much to the beauty of the scene.

On the steep sides of the mountains men and women were gathering olives. Here the olive trees assume a much larger size and better appearance than in the South western parts of France and add much to the beauty of the fore ground in a mountainous landscape for though the verdure is pale and not to be compared with that of the pine yet the trunk has great variety of form and much beauty. To collect the fruit which is now ripe black and of a very bitter taste they spread large sheets of cloth under the trees and then men ascend and knock off the fruit with poles a slight concussion or shaking is sufficient for this purpose for the ripe fruit is easily separated from the branches.

Further on we found the limestone more solid and compact being sometimes black or grey but in general white. It soon changed and appeared in a very curious and singularly stratified form. These strata were from two or three inches to above a foot in thickness and were in almost every possible direction presenting in some places acute angles in others curved lines in others short and broken spaces &c.

We had now got considerably up the mountain and the valley behind us appeared like a map. By the road side was a wild fig tree still bearing last years fruit. On the opposite mountains a flock of sheep was grazing but they seemed more like maggots than what they were. The sea was soon visible over the tops of the lower mountains and snow began to surround us. - Having arrived at the top we looked back and were amply repaid for our pains by the beauty and singularity of the scene. There was the deep valley we had left spotted with white houses & the little bridges of the river than ran through it. The sheep halfway down the mountains side and the winding road enlivened the tremendous precipices and the sea in the distance splendidly reflected the rays of a bright sun.

We found it very warm up to the highest point but when we began to descend the sharp wind quickly made us close our coats and keep in what warmth we could. We found one part of the road very dangerous being sheltered from the sun by a high rock it had become paved with ice and running on the very edge of a precipice of great depth it was considered prudent to descend and walk but by locking two wheels and putting projecting nails in the horses shoes all was conveyed safely over it. At last we reached the foot of this mountain having occupied five hours well in crossing it and early in the evening arrived at the Village (Sospelo) where we were to stop. The mountain was called something like Baurez[?].[69]

During supper an alarm of fire was given and it made me move when on putting my hand on the wall of the room we were in I found it quite hot. On going out I found that furniture and other things in the cellar of an adjoining house were on fire. The manner of extinguishing it was very philosophical and if it could be applied properly very efficacious; it was to exclude the air from the fire and suffocate it by closing up every crevice and opening with dung wet straw &c by this means it was hindered from spreading, fear was allayed and the neighbours went to rest leaving the place thus closed up. I found out afterwards that the heat of the walls was caused merely of the kitchen fire on the other side.

F. 18 We rose betimes this morning and pursued our journey to the Alps. We began to ascend immediately on leaving the village and proceeded very slowly but this slowness allowed time to enjoy the beauty of the country. The mountains were all limestone and the stratification as singular and contorted as before.

In two hours and a half we reached the top of the mountain and obtained a view more grand if possible than yesterday's. Near to us were deep vallies both to the right and left formed by mountains and rocks buried deep in the snow. The sea appeared in the distance in one direction and in another the highest of the Maritime Alps and the postillion pointed out to me a fall of snow which was taking place on the part which he said we should have to cross tomorrow. It appeared like a cloud reposing on the mountain.

There was much sulphate of lime both stratified & crystallised on the top of this mountain and also carbonate. The sulphate was tinged with various shades of lilac brown and yellowish white.

We now began to descend and after passing more icy road and an enormous flight of crows arrived at the bottom and at a small village where we breakfasted. After refreshing ourselves we proceeded our road lying on the edge of a rocky river extremely clear & green and coming down from the Alps. I never saw such fine scenery as on this part of our

---

69   Either Col de Braus or Col de Brouis.

road it was magnificence and immensity itself. The rocks often rose perpendicularly on the side of the road for many hundred feet and sometimes overhung it in the most terrific manner. In one place the way had by blasting and hewing been actually cut out of the side of a leaning rock and with the roaring river at the bottom and the opposite precipes was an inconceivably romantic situation. The whole here limestone.

After a while a town of no small size appeared before us almost suspended in the air. I endeavoured to conceive a way by which access could be gained to it but could think of nothing but ropes & pullies. The postillion however told me the pass was on the other side of the mountain. It was called Saouggio.[70]

The rocks were now slate of various shades of grey inclining to red and brown. The limestone appeared surmounting it at a great height - The bed of the river in this part was very beautifull. Formed of rocks and roughened still more by large masses of shistes[71] which had been blown into it in making the road. The water was continually agitated and opposed and the fall of the stream being very considerable gave rise to numerous cascades and waterfalls which often occurred of the height of two or three feet within 20 yards of each other; where smooth and clear the rocks appeared of beautiful colours like marble. - In a part of the road where the rocks rise to an enormous height on each side is an inscription cut in the solid stone opposite the road informing the passenger by whom and at what time this road was made.

The water which exudes from & runs down the cliffs produces on their sides enormous icicles and these by degrees become so large and heavy that unable to support themselves they fall and threaten destruction to the passing traveller[;] several of them lay in the road and the fragments were often too heavy for me to lift. We now began to get from between those cliffs and entered a narrow valley. The river had decreased much in size & the snow appeared more plentiful. At a distance we beheld Tandi[72] the end of our days journey. An eagle was soaring about in the neighbourhood of this town in search of its prey. They are very common in these parts and sometimes five or six are seen at once.

Arrived at Tandi we prepared for dinner and felt not a little disappointed when told it was Friday for their telling us was a sign they held it a fast and still more they would make us fast too and accordingly we could get nothing but eggs, egg soup, black maccaroni & vegetables.

S. 19th Rose this morning at day break which was much advanced at ½ past 5 o clk and made preparations for crossing the great mountain or Col de Tandi. At Tandi the noble road which had given such facil and

---

70   Saorge.
71   schists, a crystalline rock structure.
72   French: Tende; Italian: Tenda.

ready conveyance finished & it was necessary to prepare for another sort of travelling. Expecting it would be very cold I added to my ordinary cloathing an extra waistcoat two pair of stockings and a night cap. These with a pair of very strong thick shoes and leathern overalls I supposed would be sufficient to keep me warm.

About 9 o clock horses were put to the carriage and we proceeded towards the mountain by a road which though not so good as the one we passed was by no means bad and still continued by the river of yesterday. On each side were extensive plains covered with snow to a great depth but sufficiently hard and solid to support the men who accompanied or rather who fetched us, as they walked upon it. There were at present but two of these persons the chief and one of the sixty five composing the band. They walked on before whistling and helping and the scene so strange and singular to us never attracted their attention unless to point out to us the site of an avalanch or a dangerous place.

There was something pleasant in the face and appearance of the chief and I thought him a good specimen of the people here. He was a tall man not at all thick but his flesh seemed all muscle and strength. His dress consisted of few articles trowsers a loose waistcoat an open jacket a hairy cap very heavy soled shoes and coarse gaiters or overalls tied round his shoes to keep out the snow was all his cloathing and I found his comrades just like him. His gait was very peculiar contracted I suppose by walking constantly on the snow where a firm footing is required.

The road began to change soon after leaving Tandi and at last became nothing but ice. It was now fit for beasts of burden only: grooves had been formed in it at equal distances to receive the feet of the horses or mules and prevent their falling and though convenient to them it was to us a great evil for as the wheels fell successively into the ruts it produced a motion not only disagreeable but very dangerous to the carriage. Sir H Davy here pointed out to me the rocks of Micacious shist and I learned at the same time that Granite is always found under this rock. The only vegetation visible though there might be much under the snow was of pine trees they lifted their verdant tops above the snow and in many places broke the monotony of a white landscape.

Having passed some distance on this road we were suddenly stopped by the wheels being entangled in the snow which was full $2\frac{1}{2}$ feet high on each side of our way and it was a work of no small labour to disengage them again having at last got free we again pursued our rout. The day was fine and clear and the sun darted his burning rays with much force upon us so as even to make us throw off our great coats; and though here encompassed by fields of snow and ice they did not apparently produce any cooling effects but seemed merely to increase the splendour of a brilliant day. Rocks here Granite.

We were now joined by four or five of the gang who had advanced to meet us and to give aid if necessary on the road and in about half an hour afterwards we came to a halt and the end of the carriage road. Here on an open space the rest of the men who were to conduct and convey us and the baggage over the mountain were collected and the scene was a very pretty subject for the pencil. On one side lay three or four traineaux or sledges and further on two chaises à porter[73] or chairs mounted on sledges. Many men were engaged in unloading and reloading mules that had come over the mountain and at some distance I saw a person coming down who had crossed from the other side and who had two men to sustain him[;] this made me suppose that the passage was a very bad one and as I intended to walk to preserve some little warmth raised my expectation in no small degree.

The horses being taken off all hands set to to dismount the carriage and charge the traineaux and after some time this was done. The pieces of the carriage were placed on two sledges and the rest as the wheels boxes &c loaded five mules. In this place the barometer stood at 27 inches and the thermometer in the shade of my body was at 44° F but the instrument had been in the carriage all morning and was heated by the intense power of the sun in the fore part of the day.[74]

The traineaux with the body of the carriage had started about 12 o clk after they had been loaded ropes were fixed to them at different parts and they were consigned each traineau to about 20 men who were by main strength to haul it over the mountain. They set off with a run and loud huzzas but the mules were not ready 'till 1 o clock and as a mule driver could be better spared if wanted than a man from the sledges I kept in their company.

At 1 o clk we began to ascend the mountain and I commenced walking with a barometer in my hand the scale of which ran from 24 to 18 inches. The path quickly changed its appearance and soon became not more than 18 or 24 inches wide. Being formed by the constant tread of mules it consisted merely of a series of alternate holes in the snow each of which was 6 or 8 inches deep and 10 or 12 across. In one part of our rout the path had been formed in the snow on so steep an ascent that the surface exposed in a perpendicular direction was above four times as broad  as the width of the path. Tracks of feet were perceived crossing the mule path here and there but leading directly up to the top of the mountain. These were the steps of the persons who had taken charge of the chaises à porter and the ascent must have been a very singular one to the person carried who would often be placed in a position nearly horizontal from the steepness of the ascent. In other places the marks of the carriage traineaux were visible. They had passed over plains of snow undirected by any previous steps or aught else except the devious mule path and the

73   chaises à porteur - sedan chairs.
74   Atmospheric pressure falls with increasing altitude by about 0.001 inches of mercury
     for every one foot increase in altitude.

top of the mountain. At a distance and nearly at the top of the mountain the Chaises à Porter were just visible and a bird soaring below it the men pointed out to me as an eagle.

After some climbing and scrambling the exertion of which was sufficient to keep me very comfortably warm I reached a ruined desolate house half way up the mountain. Here we found the traineaux the men having rested themselves after this long and laborious stage were now waiting for their leader and the dram bottle. From hence the view was very extensive and very singular. The mules which I had left at a little distance behind me appeared winding up the staircase which itself towards the bottom seemed to diminish to a mere line and all was inclosed in an enormous basin and shut out from every thing but the skies. The sound of the mens voices and the mule bells was singularly clear and distinct.

After a short rest all resumed their labour and at 43' after 3 o clk I gained the summit of the mountain having been 3 hours ascending. Here at a height of more than 6000 feet above the level of the sea the thermometer was at 11° F and the barometer at 25.3 inches. The observation of the barometer was made by Sir H Davy for though the mercury oscillated in the instrument I carried it did not fall within the scale.

The summit of the mountain is very pointed and the descent consequently begins immediately on the other side but I stopped a few minutes to look around me. The view from this elevation was very peculiar and if immensity bestows grandeur was very grand. The sea in the distance stretching out apparently to infinity. The enormous snow clad mountains the clouds below the level of the eye and the immense white valley before us were objects which struck the eye more by their singularity than their beauty and would after two or three repetitions raise feelings of regret rather than of pleasure. The wind was very strong and chilling and during the short time I remained not a quarter of an hour we were envelloped in a cloud which however soon passed off and left all clear before us.

To descend was a task which though not so tedious was more dangerous than to ascend. The snow was in much greater quantity on this side the mountain than on the other and in many places where it had drifted assumed a beautifully delicate appearance. In numberless spots it was according to the men more than 20 feet deep and in descending it often received me more than half way into it. In some parts caves or hollows occur having only a small hole in the top of the apparently solid snow & those who leave the mule path and descend directly down the mountain must be particularly careful of such places least they fall into them and be lost. In descending, one of the mules missed the steps and fell rolling over and over several yards down the side of the mountain fortunately it was not hurt and by cutting a temporary path in the snow and supporting his burden on each side it was quickly brought into the right road.

After I had been descending for some time down the mountain the men with the traineaux made their appearance at the top having finished by far the most arduous part of their undertaking. They stopped only to change the arrangement of the cords and were almost immediately in motion. Their progress now was extremely quick and I thought dangerous for men and traineaux actually slid in a direct line towards the bottom of the mountain over these extensive and untried plains of snow.

About ¼ past 4 o clk we passed a little village consisting of 7 or 8 huts nearly buried in the snow. They were uninhabited and are principally intended as a refuge for the men if accidents or other circumstances should occur to detain them on the mountain during the night. At about ¼ past 5 o clk evening began to come on and the effect produced by it on the landscape was very singular for the clouds and the mountains were so blended together that it was impossible to distinguish the earth from the atmosphere. The traineaux now rapidly approached us with surprising velocity and as it began to grow dark I joined them there being the greatest number of men had I wanted aid and their hard work being finished. Just as star light came on the sounds of the evening bell of a distant village was faintly heard. They came from the place we were going to - Lanthorns were lighted and one was carried before each traineau and guided by them and a river which owed its birth to the mountain and was here of considerable size[;] we got to Leman[75] about 7 o clk in the evening and there put up for the night supper and rest being both welcome.

S. 20. The carriage being in the same state that it was yesterday and the baggage also being put upon traineaux we set off about 9 o clk in the same manner as before but on a more level road, our journey however owing to a fall of snow was much more disagreeable till about half past ten o clk when the sun shone out with much power. Some time after we had left Leman we passed on the road side a finely painted and ornamented chapel and soon after a village called Vernon[76] of considerable size and population.

Leaving Vernon we proceeded in the same way through roads or rather paths so bad and narrow that it was a matter of surprise how the carriage escaped with only a large scratch for the walls of snow here were almost as formidable as walls of stone. After a time appearances began to improve and signs of cultivation were again visible in the banked up sides of the mountains and small birds were flying about; these were to us very chearful appearances. The snow instead of being hard and dusty was soft and adhesive and the river which had commenced in the mountains and often accompanied us was now very large - We met many small [s]ledges drawn by mules. They are

---

75   Limone Piemonte.
76   Vernante.

constantly used as means of conveyance in this country above half the year - The snow still continued in great abundance and presented a dreary appearance as far as the eye could reach. The great dissimilarity betwen the quantities on this and the other side of the mountain and also between the climates is very striking and singular and exactly contrary to what I expected on entering Italy.

The valley now appeared to open considerably, the snow became much thinner and we passed through a grove of chesnut trees. There was also another tree of considerable size and something like in its winter state the chesnut called . . . (Bermuge)[77] from which oil is obtained in considerable quantities. Other signs of civilisation too were visible and made us quite happy.

The disease which is often said to originate from the drinking of snow water here made its appearance and the wen or goitre disfigured the necks of a fourth or fifth part of the people.

We now passed another village called Roubillant[78] where the snow was in much less quantity than in the former ones but still sufficient I should suppose to embarras the inhabitants. It had in many places covered the ground to the depth of 3 or 4 feet and the inhabitants to get at their houses had to cut it away from the sides forming little alleys and lanes and had thrown it into the middle of the street so that the road was often higher than the tops of the doors - After this town we came to a chapel on the road side containing some very fine looking pictures. There were three of them and appeared to deserve a more sheltered situation. These chapels are very common here. This is the fourth we have passed this morning. They are small buildings with the fronts merely closed by iron railing so that the interior which contains an altar a cross and other religious materials and ornaments suitable to the Italian style is visible. They are constantly saluted by the people (who are all catholics) as they pass them and when they have time count their beads before them.

In a short time Oubourk[79] became visible and at 2 o clock we arrived there. Here the carriage was put together again and we started with post horses at 4 o clk for Cani[80] for certainly there was nothing in this strange place to invite a stay - The view of the Alps as we left them was magnificent stretching out to the right and left till lost to the sight and ascending above the clouds that floated around them. They seemed to form an insurmountable and impassable barrier to man. We had however just proved that this appearance like many others was deceitful and when I thought on yesterdays exploit I looked at them with some thing like familiarity. Arriving at Cani we put up there for the night.

---

77   Bergamot (Citrus Bergamia); a fragrant oil, Essence of Bergamot, is prepared from
       the rind of the fruit of the tree.
78   Robilante.
79   Borgo San Dalmazzo.
80   Cuneo.

M. 21. Left Cani early with very disagreeable weather much snow being on the ground and more falling and it was also very cold. We moved in a direction almost parallel to the alps and in every position & point of view they were magnificent. Monte Viso the highest of this chain appeared at one time with three separate tier[s] of clouds on it and the summit projected considerably above the highest tier. Still further north a range of mountain tops rose above the clouds and it was easy to fancy them the outskirts of an aerial world.

Muffs seem here to be an essential article of dress so essential indeed that not only every woman but many men have them and it appears ridiculous enough to us to see a man or sometimes a woman with a little hareskin muff on one hand and a whip in the other driving a cart or a mule. Crossing the river Po we moved quickly forward on a good road and soon entered Turin.

T 22. To day we remained in Turin a city remarkable for the regularity of its streets and surpassing in this respect every other in Europe. The streets are wide and spacious and generally long and terminating in Places or Squares. The pavements are still the same for man and beast. The houses are large and regular and built with stone. Shops are plentiful and some traffic seems to be carried on. The roman steelyard is in constant and general use and a pair of scales are rarely seen except in the apothecaries shop.

This day happened to be the last of the Carnivale.[81] So I walked out in the afternoon to see what was doing in public. Towards three o clock shops shut up very rapidly and the masters betook themselves to walking gazing and the amusements now going on - Such as were determined to be cheerful in spite of appearances joined the numbers that were waltzing to the music of itinerant musicians and certainly these did not seem the least cheerful and happy part of the populace of Turin (I may perhaps add also were not the least numerous). I strolled to one place just on the skirts of the town & found it crowded by those who thus easily obtained the pleasures. It was a large clear piece of ground on the bank of a branch of the Po and resounded from end to end side to side with the harmony of a number of musical professors. The little groups into which they had formed themselves were surrounded each one by its circle of ever-moving and never-tired dancers and the spaces between these groups were filled up by a heterogeneous mixture of singers leapers boxers chesnut merchants apple-stalls beggars trees and lookers on. I fell in with one of the most worthy sets at least they claimed the pre-eminancy and it was allowed them by the other mobs. The nucleus was an enormous stone on which stood totteringly five musicians and twenty one pair were waltzing round them.

---

81   Shrove Tuesday.

Returning into the town I found that those of Turin who were superior to the vulgar amusements I have just described had resorted to the employment which custom has ascertained to be more refined and suited to their ordinary habits and occupations. That such a suitableness exists I verily believe but I think I perceived much more cheerfulness and means much better suited to produce it in the crowds I had left than in those I came to see but pride will supply many wants and food cloathing amusement and comfort are very often given up for its peculiar gratification - I found myself in a wide and spacious street of considerable length terminating at one end in a large place having a church in its centre. All the entrances into this street were guarded by soldiers and no person on horseback or in a carriage could gain admission into it except at the top a long string of carriages curricles saddle horses &c filled it and they continued to move on progressively up and down the street and round the church for several hours. It was presumed that these vehicles carried the principle persons of the town but nobody pretended to say that the owners were actually in them. One of very goodly aspect and fine appearance was pointed out to me when coming up the horses were very handsome and the coachman and footman as spruce as could be and so were the two maids in the inside - The next was not so dashing but it was empty and the third was so shabby that I did not look to see what was inside. There were however an immense number of persons who stood on each side of the street looking and gazing with great apparent satisfaction and who if they had been conscious of the comparison I was then making between the scene before me and the one I had just left would have looked down upon me with contempt & derision no doubt equal at least to that which at the same moment occupied my mind. Silly however as the whole affair was it had nearly led to circumstances of more importance. A gentleman in his curricle attended by his servant had come down one of the side streets and wished to enter the "Corso" unlawfully but was opposed by the soldier guarding the entrance. The gentleman irritated by the repulse endeavoured to force his way by rough driving. The soldier set his bayonet and stood his ground. The horse was slightly wounded and near being killed and from the pain became restive and had nearly killed his master who was in the end obliged to turn back with his wounded horse amidst the derision and laughter of the surrounding mob - As evening came on the Corso gradually broke up and the Carnivale concluded with numberless theatres and a masked ball.

W. 23. Nothing particular occurred except the being disappointed of seeing the museum here. The weather very cold indeed but clear sunshine.

T. 24. Left Turin at an early hour and took the road to Genoa. The Alps with Monte Viso were continually a part of the landscape and the Po also at one time joined in producing variety. The weather extremely cold and the wind so sharp as to condense the perspiration of the horses in hoar frost on their backs and sides. As the day advanced the Appenines came in view and in the evening we arrived at and slept at Alexandria.[82]

F. 25. This morning the weather very cold but as the sun rose becoming more tolerable and the rigour of the wind somewhat softened by his rays. About mid day we began to cross the Appenines by a very bad road so full of steps or stairs as to threaten very serious danger to the carriage. Here the sun shone extremely hot even to oppression and the snow & ice rapidly melted. We met mules to the number of more than one hundred crossing the mountains for though the road will permit the passing of carriages and large vehicles yet these beasts afford the most convenient means of conveyance. The rock consisted of beautiful green serpentine Mica slate and slate. On arriving at the top of the mountainous ridge the sea came in view and a road appeared which promised better progress than we had made for the last 3 or 4 hours. The difference in temperature between the two sides of the mountain was very striking here it was mild and pleasant and vineyards again appeared. In one part of the road the rock had been shivered and the serpentine appeared of a beautiful form & colour. Evening now came on but the road was pleasant laying partly through gardens and partly on the sea shore. Shortly the lighthouse at Genoa appeared in the distance and we soon arrived at the town and stopped.

S. 26. To day took a walk round the harbour and upon the top of the wall the view very handsome from various points. The city besides being in itself a picturesque object is finely situated and possessing the advantages of both sea and land i.e. mountains it wants nothing to form a varied and beautiful landscape. Almost every house in the town has a terrace on the roof and generally a little elevation on the terrace from which the view may be conveniently enjoyed. Orange trees appear here but in no great quantity and this year's frost has greatly injured them – Slate is employed in considerable quantities for building purposes it is often substituted for marble about the fire places and is then sometimes prettily sculptured it is of excellent service in the construction of stairs and is even at times placed edgeways to form the bars of the drain grates in the streets.

In the evening I went to the opera. The performance was for the benefit of a principal actress and in consequence an addition was made to the common course of entertainments. At a moment when the actress had completed the performance of a difficult piece of singing and had began to receive abundance of applause a shower of printed papers descended from the top of the theatre amongst the audience. Some of

82   Alessandria.

them were copies of the piece just sung and others were verses in praise of the actress. Like the rest I strived to obtain one and succeeded. After the shower of papers several pigeons were thrown one by one from the top of the theatre into the pit and some of them suffered cruel deaths. Before the evening concluded a repetition of these entertainments took place accompanied by a shower of gold (paper) with all of which the audience appeared highly delighted. The theatre was small & pretty, the performance to me very tedious.

S. 27. To day another walk about Genoa gave me further opportunities of seeing this pleasant place. I went to some gardens belonging to an englishman which were situated on the summit of a hill and from beneath an orange tree enjoyed a beautiful view of the whole city. Afterwards I looked into some of the Palaces and churches in the town. They are extremely elegant and rich abounding in every thing that can ornament & embellish. The palaces with their courts their porticoes and stairs of marble ornamented with statues and enriched with paintings cause a very high idea of the richness the luxury and the refinement of their owners or perhaps rather of their builders for Genoa is not at present what it has been. The churches are ornamented to the utmost degree paintings sculptures and gilding appear without and the front of one of them was covered with black and white marble arranged in horizontal stripes over the surface. To day the Carnivale finishes and nothing but balls theatres spectacles &c are thought of for the evening. The theatres close with the Carnivale.

T. 1. Preparations were made for departure and the carriage was put in an open boat intending to take the sea[83] to Lereche[84] or Livourne.[85]

W. 2. Much snow fell this morning which hindered our departure from this place.

T. 3. To day fine weather but dirty from the thaw and the annoyance which exist throughout the southern part of France and even to this place. A tin or copper trough is generally hung under the eaves of the houses and to get rid of the water which collects in it in rainy or snowy weather tubes project outwards from them for 2 or 3 feet and deliver it on to the heads of the passers bye below. In Genoa there are not many of these rain collectors but the roofs over hang so much as to be a great annoyance to the person below and often leaves him in doubt whether it rains hard or is quite clear.

---

83   Italian roads were very poor and not fit for carriages. Many travellers went by water when possible.
84   Lerici.
85   Livorno.

The swell on the sea is so strong as to prevent the boat from leaving the harbour and of course we remain here. In going to the sea shore to observe the waters I saw punishment inflicted on a man for stealing. A stage was erected at the crossing of two streets and on it was fixed an upright pole and a bench. The man was placed on the bench and chained by the neck to the pole on which over his head was a placard intimating that he (specifying the name profession and residence) had on such a day and at such a time taken money to a certain amount out of the house of a person whose name and residence was also stated and therefore all persons were hereby warned not to have connection or dealing with him.

F. 4 To day went with Sir H Davy to the house of a chemist to make experiments on torpedoes.[86] There were three small ones being about 5 inches long and 4 broad. They were very weak & feeble for when the water in which they were was warmed they gave but very weak shocks, so weak that I could not feel them but Sir H. Davy did. The great object was to ascertain whether water could be decomposed by the electrical power possessed by those animals: for this purpose wires were cemented into tubes and the surface of the ends only exposed as in Dr. Wollaston's method and the two extreme ends connected with plates of tin were placed in contact with the two organs of the fish. It was then irritated and often contracted apparently giving the shock but no effect on the water was perceived. However the smallness and weakness of the fish and the coldness of the season prevented any negative conclusion from being formed and it was resolved to complete the experiments in more advantageous circumstances another time. - A strong swell on the sea and the wind contrary.

S. 5 To day a large torpedo was brought to Sir H Davy but it was dead: it was about 10 inches long and 8 or 9 broad. - One of the small ones was opened. The electrical organs occupy a large part of the fish and consist of a collection of tubes parallel to each other but perpendicular to the surface of the fish and traversing nearly from the under to the upper surface[;] these tubes are filled with a gelatinous semitransparent matter of a pale pearl colour. They are situated on each side towards the head of the fish and are close to the mouth and organs of respiration[;] they occupy about a fourth part of the area of the fish or perhaps rather more.

The weather as yet against our voyage and in the afternoon a storm of thunder lightning & rain with waterspouts - A flash of lightning illuminated the room in which I was reading and I then went out on the terrace to observe the weather. Looking towards the sea I saw three waterspouts all depending from the same stratum of clouds. I ran to the sea shore on the outside of the harbour hoping they would approach

---

86   An electric fish of the ray family.

nearer but that did not happen. A large and heavy stratum of dark clouds were advancing apparently across the field of view in a westerly direction[;] from the stratum hung three water spouts one considerably to the west of me another nearly before me and the third eastward. They were apparently at nearly equal distances from each other. The one to the west was rapidly dissolving and in the same direction a very heavy shower of rain was falling but whether in the same place or nearer or more distant I could not tell: rain fell violent all the time at Genoa. The one before me was more perfect and distinct in its appearance it consisted of an extended portion of cloud very long and narrow which projected from the mass above downward in a slightly curved direction towards the sea: this part of the cloud was well defined having sharp edges and at the lower part tapering to a point. It varied its direction considerably during the time that I observed it sometimes becoming more inclined to the horizon and sometimes less; sometimes more curved and at others more direct. Beneath this projecting cloud and in a direction opposite to the point the sea appeared violently agitated; at the distance they were from me I could merely perceive a vast body of vapour rising in clouds from the water and ascending to some height but disappearing as steam would do long before it reached the point of the cloud. The elongated part apparently extended from the stratum about 2/5 or 1/2 of the distance between it and the water but no distinct and visible connexion except in effect could be perceived between the vapour of the sea and the extended cloud. Appearances were exactly the same with the third waterspout. The first disappeared very quickly. The second continued after I saw it about 10 or 12 minutes and the third 15 or 20 minutes. They continued their progressive motion with the clouds during the whole time and the third before it disappeared had advanced considerably. I should think 2 or 3 miles. The destruction and dissolution of the water spouts seemed to proceed very rapidly when it had once commenced and 3 or 4 minutes after the apparent commencement of decay it had entirely disappeared. The vapour the sea and the cloud diminished in nearly equal proportions. They were situated much farther out to sea than I at first supposed I should think 5 or 6 miles and of course what I have here noted is merely a relation of the thing as it appeared to me and is possibly very different to the real truth. During the time I remained on the Pont or Quay observing the water spouts a strong flash of lightning and a heavy peal of thunder proceeded from the same stratum of clouds.

S. 6. To day Sir H Davy made some experiments on the large dead torpedo with the galvanic battery by which he ascertained that all parts of the fish were conductors of electricity and that the gelatinous substance which filled the cells of the electrical organs were coagulated in a singular manner at the positive pole of the apparatus.

M. 7. The wind and sea being favourable we left Genoa this morning. The parting view of the town was extremely beautiful buildings mountains and water appearing disposed in the most admirable manner. The harbour forts and town were in the fore ground the Appenines behind and the Alps in the distance to the left hand beautifully radiant in the sun light. The rocks about Genoa are limestone and in some places the strata are singularly broken and disturbed. Further on the high rocky cliffs were a coarse breccia of flints (broken) cemented by limestone. About Portofino mountains of white marble occurred and continued visible for some distance in the neighbouring bay.

As the evening came on I observed a curious refraction of the mountains. The extreme ends of the distant promontories and the Alps did not appear to touch the water but seemed suspended at a little distance over it. As for instance Port

Maurice[87] at the extremity of the Maritime Alps and about 70 or 80 miles distant appeared as a long and low promontory stretching out into the sea but not in contact with it except where the altitude amounted to above a certain quantity for towards the extremity the earth disappeared to the eye before it could be hidden by the waters. This was rendered more evident from the mountainous form of that part of the promontory making it appear like a number of distinct elevations above the water. At a certain distance these elevations appeared as separate and independant spots suspended over the water for the interval between them having an altitude within the disappearing distance that part became invisible and the connexion of the whole was not perceived. I do not mean to say that a line of separation was apparently continually visible between the water and the earth but that when the earth fell within a certain degree of altitude it suddenly disappeared at the lower part. I observed also that the appearance varied considerably according as the boat was situated on the top of the waves or sank in the hollows between them for the rise of the boat on the wave often caused a part that had disappeared to become again visible. This took place a short time before sunset about ½ past 4 o clk - A short time after sunset we arrived at and put up at a miserable Auberge at Sestris.[88]

---

87   Porto Maurizio.
88   Sestri Levante.

T. 8. Found the ground this morning covered with snow much having fallen in the night. The sea was very rough and we remained here.

W. 9. The sea still so much agitated the weather so rainy & the wind so contrary that we remain where we are.

T. 10. Snow has fallen in the night. It is rainy and our departure as yet impracticable - Whilst looking towards the sea I observed a singular motion in part of a large cloud and judge that a water spout was forming. A portion of the cloud projected downwards from about the middle of the under surface. This and the surrounding parts were in violent agitation. The vapour of the projecting piece seemed continually to roll upwards and yet it did not diminish but was apparently supplied by some invisible means at the lower end. That part of the cloud too which was in the vicinity of this agitated piece approached rapidly towards it and appeared to combine and mix with it at the upper part. In about 5 minutes it disappeared and the cloud gradually passed over the horizon. This was about half past 6 o clk.

At 7 o clk I saw a water spout the phenomena were nearly the same as with those I saw before the large dark cloud, the curved spout much longer than in the former instances and the vapour of the sea, but after a few moments this spout appeared very evidently tubular and an ascending motion appeared in the upper part of the sides. The clouds were not particularly dense or strong about the head of the water spout but on the contrary rather fainter there than elsewhere in the same mass. The course was apparently from east to west and the distance I thought about three or four miles. In about five minutes it disappeared. An hour afterwards we had much snow and hail and the weather then seemed clearing up.

F. 11. Rainy weather sea rough and the wind south. In the evening hail thunder & lightning. A sailor brought to the inn a curious little fish that he had caught in his net. He called it a sea horse and it had certainly a great resemblance to that animal in the form of the head.

S. 12. Wind this morning from the north and the weather fine but the sea rough yet. Took a walk on the sea shore which was very rocky and steep but a good road had been cut in the rocks. Limestone and slate the slate with many veins of calcareous spar running at times for many yards though not thicker than a shilling.

S. 13. Rose this morning at 1 o clk and got on board as quickly as possible. At 2 o clk we left Sestris with a wind which though in a favourable direction was somewhat too strong. The first part of our voyage by moonlight though by no means particularly pleasant far surpassed the latter part. After much delay from accident gusts of wind &c and not without some danger we at last reached Lereche tired cold and bruised.

M. 14. Left Lereche this morning about 12 o clk with oxen attached to the carriage the post horses being all engaged. The mountains here are covered by olive trees. Limestone and slate are the rocks of the country. We crossed the river [   ] in a boat which was thrust over by poles and at about 5 o clock arrived and stopped at Sarzanna.[89]

T. 15. Pursued our road to Lucca. In the morning we passed the mountains of Carrara which constitute a part of the Appenines and from whence very beautiful statuary marble is obtained. This country well deserves to be called the land of oil and wine for we passed through forests of vines and olive trees. The vineyards must appear very beautiful here in the summer and autumn. They generally mark out the edges and boundaries of the land with them and each proprietor further divides and partitions his grounds with rows of them. They are conducted upwards about 15 or 18 feet and then arranged in festoons and drapery from one tree to another.
The rocks of the road we passed over were marble of the finest and whitest kind very beautiful specimens could easily have been collected. This morning we left the french territories and entered the Neapolitan dominions and the joy and even rapture with which we were received were very pleasant to Englishmen. In the afternoon we arrived at Lucca and found a vast concourse of people on the outside of the town expecting and waiting for the English General.[90] In the town every house was decorated with flags and tapestry and at night an illumination took place which though pretty general was nothing to what was expected on the morrow.

---

89   Sarzana.
90   Lord William Bentinck (1774-1839), commander of a British force passing through Tuscany on its way to Genoa. Lucca had been under the rule of Napoleon's sister Elisa, Princess of Lucca and Piombino and Grand Duchess of Tuscany. After her departure in 1814, it was occupied by Neapolitan troops.

W. 16. Left Lucca for Florence passed through a fine & fertile country where from the number of canals dykes trenches &c irrigation was apparently pursued to a great extent. Weather fine. Appenines a beautiful object on our left hand. We arrived early at Florence that celebrated city for genius. The Hotel we stopped at seemed a Palace both outside and inside.

T. 17. A short walk round the town. The streets are paved with flagstones of all sizes and shapes so that walking is far more comfortable and cleaner than in the towns we have yet passed through. The river Arno which runs through the city is wide but shallow and muddy. It is crossed by four bridges. One of them called [   ]^{91} is a very beautiful piece of architecture it has three arches and has an air so light and free one can scarcely imagine it to be of stone. In France and Italy it appears that Quays are the constant attendant of a river in passing through a town: in Florence they are not wanting and add much to the beauty & convenience of the place.

F. 18. Another walk. I came to the Cathedral a large and magnificent building covered except in the front with black and white marble arranged in columns pannels &c. The front is not finished and has been painted temporily in an architectural style but the weather has nearly obliterated this embellishment and the bare wall appears forming a singular contrast with the rest of the building. The inside is but poorly ornamented except the altar and strikes the senses only from its magnitude and the beautiful windows of painted glass.

Close to the Cathedral is (Tour del Giotto ?)^{92} a square building with a small base but rising to a great height. It is covered with white marble and ornamented by the inlaying of other colours. The sculptures and medallions on it are very beautiful. I have not yet had the pleasure of mounting to the top from whence is to be had as is said the finest possible view of Florence & the environs. Opposite to the cathedral is a small building called the Baptistry the doors of which are of bronze and most beautifully cast.

There are some beautiful statues and a bronze in the place before the old palace and between the Palace of Justice and the Post Office. The Bronze is a fine figure of Perseus with the head of Medusa and on the pedestal of the statue a tablet of the same metal represents him slaying the dragon &c.

The court of the Palace of justice has a very striking appearance from the ornamental columns which support it and which appear like enlarged chinese ivory work.

---

91   Possibly Ponte Santa Trinità.
92   The Campanile di Giotto.

M. 21. Went with Sir H Davy to the Academy del'
Cimento[93]: saw the library which was very small then saw
the gardens which are conveniently arranged and
afterwards saw the rooms and apparatus. Here was much
to excite interest. In one place was Galileo's first telescope
that with which he discovered Jupiter's satellites. It was
a simple tube of wood and paper about $3\frac{1}{2}$ feet long with
a lens at each end, the field of view very small. Here was
also the first lens which Galileo made: it was set in a very
pretty frame of brass with an inscription in latin on it. The lens itself is
cracked across. The great burning glass of the Grand Duke of Tuscany
a very powerful instrument was here also. The Academy has abundance
of electrical apparatus one electrical machine was made of red velvet the
rubber being formed of gilt leather. In a glass case were preserved some
Leyden phials perforated in an extraordinary manner: one of them had
been broken through by the discharge of a battery in such a manner that
a hole of $\frac{1}{4}$ of an inch in diameter had been formed. On the edge of the
hole the glass was absolutely pulverised and cracks extended to the
distance of $\frac{1}{4}$ of an inch from it beyond which nothing particular was
visible: the tin foil had been burnt off a space larger than the extent of
the cracks. Another jar had also been perforated and a hole of some size
formed but the most particular thing was the combustion of the tin foil
which had taken place from the hole to the bottom of the jar and a
surface of about seven square inches exposed. This was on the outside;
on the inside the foil was but little damaged.

There was also a numerous collection of magnets of various forms
and combinations. An enormous one which was enclosed in a box
supported a weight of 150 lbs.

Sir H Davy afterwards went into the Laboratory to which place I
attended him and made various experiments on Iodine.

T. 22. The day principally employed in the Laboratory.

W. 23. The same as yesterday.

T. 24. Prepared things to day for the combustion of the diamond
in oxygen tomorrow if the weather prove fine. The Duke's great lens was
brought out and placed in the garden and its effect observed on wood &c
which it instantly inflamed - Afterwards I walked round the upper rooms
of the museum containing specimens and illustrations of the Natural
history and was highly gratified. The anatomical illustrations are nearly

93   The Accademia del Cimento had been active in Florence between 1657 and 1667, and
      the books and instruments used by its members were given in 1771 by the Grand
      Duke of Florence to the Museo di Storia Naturale where Faraday saw them. An
      unsuccessful attempt to revive the Academy was made in 1801.

all formed of wax at least those intended to exemplify the muscles nerves and less durable parts of the body[94]. They are modelled and coloured with the utmost exactness. The various part[s] of the body are represented distinct and separate and in many states they are nicely arranged upon silk and sattin and preserved in glass cases themselves clean and free from dust. The more durable parts are sometimes represented in ivory and carved bone and sometimes by the bones themselves though wax also gives its aid. Over each anatomical specimen is suspended a fine drawing with references and explanations of the parts below. There are also many natural specimens singular and curious. The rooms appropriated to botany are furnished with beautiful imitations in wax of flowers which are also represented again in pictures the place having every appearance of a beautiful garden. - The insects are very numerous and in all the different states such as the egg the chrysalis the worm and the fly. There are also a considerable number of birds and with many of them the nests and eggs. Other rooms contain many singular & curious fishes. The shells are beautiful and arranged in admirable order and with corals sponges and other marine productions form an interesting department. Reptiles are not wanting and among them are some enormous snakes. The mineral kingdom shines with great splendour and the specimens vie with those of any other branch of natural history not even excepting the birds. There are some handsome tables inlaid with marbles porphyries serpentine jaspers agates lapis lazula &[c]. There are a vast number of specimens of native gold some beautiful vases of fluor spar from Derbyshire three fine cups of chrystal malachite cut into boxes and an abundance of precious stones. These last were generally set in gold or silver of an appropriate form and appeared to great advantage.

The last room contains some singular specimens of carving and modelling representing the horrors of death in the Plague and in a sepulchre. There were some Egyptian mummies in the room one of them opened.

F. 25. This being annunciation day was held as a grand fête. The country people flocked into the town in their best attire the women ornamented with enormously large ear rings and an abundance of gold and silver lace about the head. About 11 o clock I went to the Cathedral and heard Te Deum sung at the conclusion of which the cannon again fired. The sound of the trumpet in so large an inclosed place produced a striking effect on the mind - the music beautiful.

---

94   In Florence a laboratory of the Museo di Storia Naturale under Felice Fontana (1730-1805) became a centre for the study of anatomy. Life-sized anatomical models were copied directly from corpses dissected for the purpose. Between 1770 and 1890, more than forty whole life-sized bodies and thousands of anatomical pieces were made in the workshop of the museum. Many of the models can still be seen in the Museo Zoologico 'La Specola'.

Afterwards went to the Laboratory and ascertained that the Duke's burning glass would not fuse platina of which metal the cradle for the diamond was formed. Towards the evening walked to the Corso - similar to that at Turin on the last day of the Carnivale - The corso commenced at the Cathedral and terminated at the Church of Annunciation. Stalls and booths stood along each side of the street forming a fair which commencing today will continue three days. Entered the church which is the richest and most ornamented of any in the city. In the evening cannon again.

S. 26. Experiments at the Academy on Iodine.

S. 27 To day we made the grand experiment of burning the diamond and certainly the phenomena presented were extremely beautiful and interesting. A glass globe containing about 22 cubical inches was exhausted of air and filled with very pure oxygen gas procured from oxymuriate of potash. The diamond was supported in the centre of this globe by a rod of platinum to the top of which a cradle or cup was fixed pierced full of holes to allow a free circulation of the gas about the diamond. The Duke's burning glass was the instrument used to apply heat to the diamond. It consists of two double convex lenses distant from each other about 3½ feet. The large lens is about 14 or 15 inches in diameter, the small one about 3 inches in diameter. The instrument is fixed in the centre of a round table and is so arranged to admit of elevation or depression or any adjustment required at pleasure by means of the second lens. The focus is very much reduced and the heat when the sun shine[s] brightly rendered very intense. The instrument was placed in an upper room of the museum and having arranged it at the window the diamond was placed in the focus and anxiously watched. The heat was thus continued at intervals for ¾ of an hour (it being necessary to cool the globe at times) and during that time it was thought that the diamond was slowly diminishing and becoming opaque. Now we had only a partial spectrum for the upper part of the window obstructed the sun's rays but having sunk the whole of the apparatus it was again exposed and a very strong heat obtained. On a sudden Sir H Davy observed the diamond to burn visibly and when removed from the focus it was found to be in a state of active and rapid combustion. The diamond glowed brilliantly with a scarlet light inclining to purple and when placed in the dark continued to burn for about four minutes. After cooling the glass heat was again applied to the diamond and it burned again though not nearly so long as before. This was repeated twice more and soon after the diamond became all consumed. This phenomenon of actual and vivid combustion which has never been observed before was attributed by Sir H Davy to the free access of air, it became more dull as carbonic acid gas formed and did not last so long. The globe and contents were put bye for future examination.

M. 28. To day we endeavoured to repeat the experiment of yesterday but the sun had sank too low and sufficient heat could not be obtained. The experiment was then made substituting chlorine for oxygen but no change of the diamond was produced. The platina was slightly acted on and a cork used to support the prop [?] very much corroded but no combination of carbon and chlorine was effected.

T. 29. This morning the diamond which we had ineffectually endeavoured to burn yesterday was brought out and being again exposed in the focus as before produced by a bright & powerful sun soon exhibited signs of strong electricity and a few small fillaments which floated in the gas were variously attracted and repelled by it. In a short time a thin slip of platina used to fasten the diamond in was observed to fuse and on taking the globe from the focus the diamond was seen in a state of intense ignition and combustion it continued burning for some time and when extinguished was again ignited by the application of the lens and burnt as before. This was repeated five times after which no visible signs of combustion or diminution could be perceived. Having applied the heat for some time longer it was was at length taken away and the temperature reduced to the same point as at the commencement of the experiment but no vapour nor any signs of the formation of water could be perceived. A portion of the gas was then put into a curved tube and decomposed by potassium charcoal was liberated and no other substance but the charcoal and the oxygen could be found in the gas formed. Lime water was then introduced and the carbonate of lime precipitated carefully gathered washed and preserved for further analysis and investigation.

W. 30. A diamond was to day exposed in the focus of the instrument in an atmosphere of carbonic acid to ascertain whether carbonic oxide could be thus formed but after exposure to the heat from 12 till 1 o clk no change could be perceived nor had the diamond lessened in weight.

T. 31. Went to the Gallery but was too late to see the paintings. Various experiments on Iodine and chloreonic acid.

S. 2. Another diamond was burned in oxygen gas for the purpose of ascertaining whether any azote or other gas unabsorbable by water was given off but all the circumstances were against such a supposition. The apparatus was very simple and convenient a small globe with a neck was filled entirely with water and then 2/3 with oxygen gas. The diamond fixed on the end of its support was introduced and the globe transferred by means of a wine glass to the lens. When heated the diamond burned as in the former cases giving out a fine scarlet light inclining to purple and extreme heat. The globe was then allowed to cool to its former temperature but no apparent change of volume had occurred though the water must have absorbed a little carbonic acid gas (the volume was not noticed with precision) a solution of lime and afterwards of caustic potash was then introduced into the globe and the carbonic acid removed then by adding nitrous gas to the same volume of the remaining gas and the oxygen used a portion of which had been preserved it was found that the diminution was exactly the same and the remainder very small in both cases so that nothing but carbonic acid gas had been formed and as yet it appears that the diamond is pure carbon. An experiment was then made on plumbago in an apparatus similar to the one used in the first instance and all care taken to exclude water at the commencement of the operation. On applying the heat fumes became visible and the surface of the plumbago fused afterwards seeming to undergo no further alteration by a further continuance of the heat it was taken away and the temperature reduced to the original point. The formation of water was immediately evident the upper part of the globe being opaque with the condensed fluid. From these experiments according to Sir H Davy it is probable that diamond is pure carbon and the black compounds such as plumbago carbon &c combinations of carbon and hydrogen. I should observe that in the experiment of to day with the diamond 4/5 of the oxygen were consumed and converted into carbonic acid. Having finished these experiments we bade adieu for a time to the Academy del' Cimento and prepared to part for Rome.

S. 3. Left Florence this morning with regret for in no place since I left England have I been so comfortable and happy. The country very fine the cultivation principally olives and vines at least they were at this time the prominent objects. The country was limestone compact friable and at times almost earthy at which times the banks of the road were full of stalactites in various position being formed during the filtration of rain & springs through the soil. Further on a loose friable breccia. We arrived in good time at Sienna[95] and stopped there.

Walked out to the Cathedral. The building most worthy of notice in the town and indeed well worthy of notice. It is of great magnitude and covered externally with black and white marble. The front is very rich and beautiful being ornamented with a profusion of gold and sculptures. The steps up to the entrance are all of marble and the space before the door is chiselled with various desings drawn from scripture history. The pavement of the Church is a mixture of mosaic and chiselled work and the designs on it are well executed. The mosaic is covered with boards. In a space uncovered for my observation a very lively design of Moses at the Rock was executed & had a singular effect in such a situation. The pillars which supported the roof were of marble and in their form gothic being apparently fourfold &c. The library[96]

95   Siena.
96   The Libreria Piccolomini.

contained many beautifully illuminated missals. There is here a beautiful group of the three graces in white marble. It was found in digging the foundations of the church and is much injured. - Much more was to be seen here and having seen it I returned home to bed & rest.

M. 4. Left Sienna at an early hour. Country well cultivated rocks limestone. - Road first hilly then became flat a calcareous breccia lying beneath. As we advanced the road presented appearances of a volcanic nature and Sir H Davy thought a mountain just before us must be an extinct volcano it proved to be such and presented many interesting circumstances. The post house where we stopped was at the foot of this mountain and though very dirty smokey and filled with Neapolitan soldiers it was our retreat for the night. We then ascended the mountain which was not large on the top of it a smaller elevation arose the summit and crater of a volcano. This part was of an irregular truncated conical form and was surmounted by the ruins of an old Tuscan castle. The summit was lava & pumice of various kinds, below under the lava basalt occurred split irregularly in a perpendicular direction. There were many cavities in the basalt some of them contained very minute cubical crystals of a black colour and opaque in others were larger semitransparent white and prismatical crystals. These Sir H Davy thought to have been formed by the cooling of a substance rendered fluid by heat. In one part a piece of a stone apparently granite appeared in the basalt it seemed to have been fused. The lower part of the mountain and the adjacent plain was covered with blocks of basalt & lava.

T. 5. Continued to advance through a country entirely volcanic and abounding with fragments of basalt and lava. The mountains were singularly ridged and rifted on their south & western sides as if cut into their present form by enormous torrents: those sides are also by much the steepest and are nearly bare of vegetation indeed cultivation appears altogether to be in a low state here though generally there is a good soil. The soil is from decomposing basalt & lava. They appear in every state here from the perfect rocks to the perfect soil - Now the country was composed of basalt full of Luicites.[97] They were frequently more than half an inch across. In one place it was columnar the column small considerably inclined to the horizon of various lengths and five and six sided. To this succeeded a great variety of lavas puzzolanas and coloured earths decking the road with a great variety of colours. In this part of our route we observed many caves and holes cut in the sides of the road some of them were of considerable size having two or three entrances for what purpose they were formed is not known.[98] The Lake of Bolsanna[99]

---

97   Leucite, a relatively rare mineral found in volcanic rocks.
98   The caves were dwellings which were still inhabited in relatively recent times.
99   Bolsena, the largest lake of volcanic origin in Italy, is actually about 42 miles in
      circumference.

which broke on the sight after a change of horses at [   ] was beautiful. It is about 30 miles round and is in a country abounding in verdure. It contains two islands both of which are inhabited. In one part of the road on the borders of this lake a hill of basaltic columns appears. They are very regular in their form and size all hexangular considerably inclined to the horizon and in some places they appear curved. They are supposed to be the result of a volcano & by some even the lake itself presents but the crater of a mountain which formerly sent forth fire. On leaving the borders of the lake we passed through a forest of oak trees of considerable size & fine appearance. The basalt was here in a decomposing state and in many places of the purest white colour.

W. 6. Pursued the road to Rome over a country still volcanic and offering Basalt & lava continually to the eyes. As the day advanced and we began to get a clear view of the Vale of the Tiber we anxiously looked out for the first glimpse of Rome. We passed on the roadside an antient tomb and several ruins of enormously massive brick work. On turning a hill we saw the upper part of St Peters. We now drew near to that antient city crossed the Tiber and entered the environs and in a short time passed through Porta Popule in old times the Porta Flaminien.[100] This gate at least the external part & design of it is of modern work. It was rebuilt in the middle of the 16th Century after the design of M A Buonarotti.

On passing the gate a very impressing and magnificent view of Rome appears. You are in a large open place from where radiate three long and spacious streets. In the middle of the place is an enormous Egyptian obelisque[101] which according to the old story ready for every traveller was first raised by Sesostris king of Egypt in the city of Hieropolis from thence it was brought to Rome by Augustus and erected in the great circus of the old city. It was removed a second time and placed in its present situation by Sixtus 5th[102] under the direction of D Fontana.[103] It is formed of red granite is 99 french feet in height and is covered with hieroglyphics.

The openings of the three streets which are in perspective are separated by two churches of similar and beautiful architecture. We took the street on the left hand and went to a hotel in the Piazza di Spagna. This place is known for the beauty of the staircase which ascends from it to the church of the Trinity situated on the summit of Mount

---

100   Porta del Popolo, earlier Porta Flaminia.
101   This obelisk in the Piazza del Popolo was raised in front of the Temple of the Sun
       in Heliopolis by Pharaohs Rameses II and Merneptah. It was brought to Rome by
       Augustus for the Circus Maximus and in 1589 was moved to its present position.
102   Pope, 1585-90.
103   Domenico Fontana (1543-1607), architect and engineer, was responsible for moving
       several obelisks in Rome.

Pencius.[104]   At the summit of the stair case & before the church is another Egyptian obelisk formed also of granite and covered with sculptures.   At the foot of the stairs is a beautiful fountain called Barcacchia its figure being that of a boat.

Having arrived at the Hotel in good time I afterwards walked to S[t] Peters of which more anon if I am able - In going I crossed the Tiber by a handsome bridge called Ponti del Angelo.[105]   It was originally built by the Romans in the time of Adrian[106] and their work may be seen in the interior of the arches it has since been repaired and embellished by Clement 9th.[107]   At the foot of the bridge is a building now a fort called La Chateau S[t] Ange[108] but formerly the Mausoleum of the Emperor Adrian. It must have been a magnificent structure when perfect.

In returning home passed by the column of Antoninus.[109]   It stands on the site of the antient forum. Was erected by the Senate in honor of Marc Aurelius for important victories which are sculptured in a spiral line on the column.   It is of the Doric order is 148 feet high and is ascended by a staircase of 190 steps within. The material is white marble & it is at present surmounted by a statue in Bronze Dore of the Apostle Paul placed there by Pope Sixtus 5th.[110]

At a short distance from the Place di Colonne is le Place di Monti Citario in the middle of which stands the obelisque solaire d'Auguste brought by that Emperor from Hieropolis to Rome.[111]   It is of red granite has been much injured but is now repaired though to the destruction of many of the hieroglyphics with which it was covered. It is 90 french feet high & is capped by a globe of gilt bronze.

From thence I went to the Fountains of Trevi a work perhaps the finest of its kind in the world for the abundance of the water and the quantity and excellence of the sculptures.   It and indeed Rome itself is supplied with water from some springs about 9 miles from the city. These waters were first brought to Rome by Agrippa[112] son of Augustus who built a subterranean conduit 14 miles in length.   This conduit has

---

104   Monte Pincio.
105   Ponte Sant' Angelo.
106   Hadrian, Emperor, AD 117-38.
107   Pope 1667-69.
108   Castel Sant' Angelo.
109   The column was built between AD 176 and 193 to honour Marcus Aurelius (Emperor 161-80).   It is in the Piazza Colonna.   An erroneous inscription added in 1589 attributed the column to Antoninus Pius (Emperor AD 86-161).
110   Pope 1585-90.
111   This obelisk of Psammeticus in the Piazza di Montecitorio was brought by Augustus to the Campus Martius where it was used as a sundial. It fell over after a fire and was re-erected by Pope Pius VI in 1792.
112   Marcus Vipsanius Agrippa (c.63-12 BC), leading supporter (and son-in-law) of the Emperor Augustus in defeating Mark Antony, in organizing the provinces of the empire, and in restoring and improving the city of Rome.   He reconditioned the sewers, added two new aqueducts, public baths and other buildings.

been rebuilt and repaired at various times and still preserves its original use and distinction.

T. 7. Walked about the City to gain a general and local knowledge of it - Many remains of antiquity - indeed innumerable. Went into a booksellers shop to enquire for an Italian and English dictionary but could not find one. Went into the workshop of a bookbinder and saw there the upper part of a fine corinthian pillar of white marble which he had transformed into a beating stone of great beauty. Found my former profession carried on here with very little skill neither strength nor elegance being attained.

F. 8. Passed the day - nothing particular.

S. 9. Rose early this morning and took a chance walk. Passed the Corso & column of Antoninus and came to the column of Trajan[113] the finest of the kind that is in existence or ever has been. It stands in the middle of the antient Forum of Trajan and was raised by the Senate & people of Rome in honor of that Emperor. It is of white grecian marble as from the base to the summit of the statue of St Peter that now stands upon it is 132 feet in height. The diameter below is 11 feet 2 inches and above 10 feet. In the interior are 183 marble steps each above 2 feet long on the top is a gallery from whence a beautiful view is to be had of Rome. Formerly a bronze statue of Trajan surmounted it. The column is covered with sculptures of exquisite beauty representing the various battles and victories of Trajan. The figures are nearly 2 feet in height and amount in the whole to 2500 besides a vast number of beasts and other objects. They are arranged in a line round the column commencing at the base and mounting to the summit of the pillar being separated by a spiral line of 23 turns.

The Forum of Trajan was formerly the finest and richest place in Rome. It contained four triumphal arches various porticoes and statues of bronze and was surrounded by a grande balustrade. At present these edifices and ornaments are in ruins and their remains lie buried in the ground. The earth has collected in this place so much during the space of time that has elapsed since the erection of the pillar that the pedestal was entirely covered & sunk in it. Lately a small square pit was opened around it to exhibit its sculptured beauties and at present works are going on to clear away the whole of the earth and make the space open and clear and the view of the pillar uninterrupted. These operations were begun by Sixtus 5th and go on slowly still.

From this column I went to the Flavian Ampitheatre but had little time to spend there.

---

113   Emperor AD 98-117.

S. 10. Writing all day.

Letter to Mother[114]

Rome: April 14, 1814

My dear Mother,

It is with singular pleasure I commence writing after so long a silence and the pleasure is greatly increased by the almost certainty that you will get my letter. We are at present in a land of friends and where every means is used to render the communication with England open and unobstructed. Nevertheless this letter will not come by the ordinary route but by a high favour Sir H. Davy will put it with his own and it will be conveyed by a particular person.

I trust that you are well in health and spirits and that all things have gone right since I left you . . . Mr Riebau and fifty other friends would be inquired after could I but have an answer. You must consider this letter as a kind of general one, addressed to that knot of friends who are twined round my heart; and I trust that you will let them all know that though distant I do not forget them and that it is not from want of regard that I do not write to each singly but from want of convenience and propriety; indeed it appears to me that there is more danger of my being forgot than of my forgetting. The first and last thing in my mind is England, home and friends. It is the point to which my thoughts still ultimately tend and the goal to which, looking over intermediate things, my eyes are still directed. But on the contrary in London you are all together, your circle being little or nothing diminished by my absence; the small void which was formed on my departure would soon be worn out and, pleased and happy with one another, you will seldom think of me. Such are sometimes my thoughts but such do not rest with me; an innate feeling tells me that I shall not be forgot and that I still possess the hearts and love of my mother, my brother, my sisters and my friends. When Sir H. Davy first had the goodness to ask me whether I would go with him, I mentally said, 'No, I have a mother, I have relations here.' And I almost wished that I had been insulated and alone in London but now I am glad that I have left some behind me on whom I can think and whose actions and occupations I can picture in my mind. Whenever a vacant hour occurs I employ it by thinking on those at home. Whenever present circumstances are disagreeable I amuse myself by thinking on those at home. In short when sick when cold when tired the thoughts of those at home are a warm and refreshing balm to my heart. Let those who think such thoughts useless vain and paltry think so still; I envy them not their more refined and more estranged feelings, let them look

---

114   Text from **BJ** 123-126, no MS survives.

about the world unemcumbered by such ties and heart-strings and let them laugh at those who, guided more by nature, cherish such feelings. For me I still will cherish them in opposition to the dictates of modern refinement as the first and greatest sweetness in the life of man.

I have said nothing as yet to you, dear mother, about our past journey which has been as pleasant and agreeable (a few things excepted, in reality nothing) as it was possible to be. Sir H. Davy's high name at Paris gave us free admission into all parts of the French dominions and our passports were granted with the utmost readiness. We first went to Paris and stopped there two months, afterwards we passed in a southerly direction through France to Montpellier on the borders of the Mediterranean. From thence we went to Nice, stopping a day or two at Aix on our way, and from Nice we crossed the Alps to Turin in Piedmont. From Turin we proceeded to Genoa which place we left afterwards in an open boat and proceeded by sea towards Lerici. This place we reached after a very disagreeable passage and not without apprehensions of being overset by the way. As there was nothing there very enticing we continued our route to Florence and after a stay of three weeks or a month left that fine city and in four days arrived here at Rome. Being now in the midst of things curious and interesting something arises every day which calls for attention and observations. The relics of ancient Roman magnificence, the grandeur of the churches and their richness also - the difference of habits and customs each in turn engages the mind and keeps it continually employed. Florence too was not destitute of its attractions for me and in the Academy del Cimento and the museum attached to it is contained an inexhaustible fund of entertainment and improvement; indeed during the whole journey new and instructive things have been continually presented to me. Tell B. I have crossed the Alps and the Apennines, I have been at the Jardin des Plantes, at the museum arranged by Buffon, at the Louvre among the chefs-d'oeuvre of sculpture and the masterpieces of painting, at the Luxembourg palace amongst Rubens' works, that I have seen a GLOWWORM!!! water-spouts torpedo the museum at the Academy del Cimento as well as St Peter's and some of the antiquities here and a vast variety of things far too numerous to enumerate.

At present I am in very good health and so far is travelling from disagreeing with me that I am become somewhat heavier and thicker than when I left England. I should have written to you long ago but I had no hopes of getting a letter conveyed but at present I conclude that you will surely have this. I have a thousand things more to say but do not know how to select one from the other so shall defer them all to a more convenient opportunity. When you write into the country remember me, if you please, to all friends there and more particularly to those to whom I have written. At present I bid farewell for a time to all friends wishing them much happiness.

I am, dear Mother, with earnest wishes for your health and welfare your dutiful son,

M. FARADAY

P.S. There is no certain road open at present by which you can write to me so that, much as I wish it, it must be deferred a little longer. We have heard this morning that Paris was taken by the Allied troops on March 31 and as things are we may soon hope for peace but at present all things are uncertain. Englishmen are here respected almost to adoration and I proudly own myself as belonging to that nation which holds so high a place in the scale of European Powers.

Adieu, dear Mother, at present. Your dutiful son,

M. FARADAY

Faraday's Journal

_M. 11. T. 12. W. 13. T. 14._ Still writing and nothing seen worthy of notice. I forgot to notice the ceremonies of last Thursday in commemoration of the death of the Saviour which were very brilliant in St Peters and many other churches. Towards the evening the illumination of the churches for which preparations had been making for two days took place and St Peters presented a magnificent sight. A large cross was suspended over the middle of the aisle nearly under the centre of the dome and illuminated in a brilliant and perfect manner on all sides. The effect it produced on the mind on entering the church was singular and powerful. In the chapel of our saviour was an illumination consisting of above two thousand wax candles of great size and every thing was arranged for the reception of the pious or curious. The various religious societies in the city came in procession by turns with lighted tapers and chaunting to give homage and the whole city appeared engaged in the service of religion. On the Saturday after at about 10 o clk a general firing of all the pistol guns &c &c in the town commenced and continued for nearly two hours, the people taking this method of expressing their joy for the resurrection.

_F. 15._ Rose early and walked to the ampitheatre by the Capitol and the Forum - The Coliseum[115] or Flavian Ampitheatre was erected by the Emperor Flavian Vespasian[116] on his return from a war against the jews in the year 72 A D and it is said that he employed 12000 of his

---

115   Colosseum.
116   Flavius Vespasianus, Emperor AD 69-79.

hebrew captives in the construction of the Edifice which was raised in five years but others say it was Titus[117] the son of Vespasian who raised the building and who dedicated it to his father with the destruction of 5000 animals of all kinds which were slain by each other or by men.

This enormous edifice externally presents where it is perfect three ranges of arches raised one on the other surmounted by a high and enormous wall demi-columns are placed between the arches which support a grand and massive entablature. Each range consists of 80 arches & it was by these and by forty windows or openings in the upper part of the wall that light was admitted into the galleries and interior of the covered parts. Each of the arches of the first or lowest range formed an entrance to steps which led to the lower ranges of seats and to the upper galleries. The entrances were numbered in regular order except in one instance where between the arches XXXVIII and XXXIX there is one unnumbered and which wants also the whole of the entablature. It is supposed that this entrance was appropriated to the Emperor's use and that the want of an entablature is owing to the former existence of a Portico now destroyed - The form of this edifice is oval. It is 1641 french feet in circumference and 157 in height. The arena is also of the same form length 285 feet: breadth 182 feet: circumference 748 feet.

This edifice has gradually by the hand of time assumed an aspect of singular beauty and great picturesque effect. Above one half of the external ranges of arches and the wall above them has fallen to the ground and the stones have been made use of in the construction of other edifices indeed a part has been demolished for the latter purpose hence it is that part of the interior of the galleries is laid open to view and the high wall which remains appears on the other side overtopping them. It is possible to mount over the ruins to the upper gallery but the exploit is not advisable and for the convenience of the more careful wooden stairs have been erected which carry nearly as high. It is from this upper station that a view fit to give a proper idea of the magnitude of the building can be obtained: on looking down the arena appears at an immense depth beneath our feet and the whole range of ruined seats and arches are laid out as in a map: on looking up the inclosing wall is still seen behind rising to an enormous height. Observing from this point the state of the interior of the building it is seen that in very few places only are the antient seats visible the arches and galleries that formerly supported them being the visible objects. These are in some places formed of brick in others of stone and are interspersed with and covered by trees and shrubs of various kinds vegetating with great luxurience thus presenting the remains of antiquity in their most attractive though melancholy form and would make one reluctant even if it were possible to lose present beauties in the renovation of a former state.

---

117   Emperor AD 79-81

There are two grand entrances into the arena one at each end of the longer axis. At present it is possible to enter only by one of them the other being filled with water. The earth has in ages incroached so much on this ground that the level was several feet above the antient level Whilst the french had possession of this country they instituted works to clear away this incumbrance and in so doing discovered various cavities and passages and the plat[118] of the arena at present filled with water. They were opened that correct plans might be taken of them and now constitute pools and canals. Endeavours have been made for the last 6 months without success to get out the water. These efforts are continued by the Romans, but not with so much vigour as before.

In memory of the number of persons professing the christian religion who suffered here in former times fourteen little chapels have been erected round the arena at equal distances and near one of the grand entrances is a house belonging to a religious fraternity.

In one part of the Ampitheatre the upper galleries are so perfect that one may walk along them for a considerable distance and the view gained from them of Rome and the surrounding country is very interesting and extensive.

The exterior of this building is entirely stone. The interior is partly stone and partly brick. The bricks are well burnt & hard and are what we should call thick tiles. The cement between the bricks is very good and hard but that of the stone work still harder. The architecture is doric ionic and corinthian. - It is calculated that the seats would formerly contain 87000 persons and the entrances in the interior of the building having a view of the arena and some spaces above the seats allowed room for 20000 more.

Near to the Coliseum stands the triumphal arch of Constantine being of all the arches remaining the richest and best preserved. It was erected and dedicated by the Senate and people of Rome to Constantine the great in memory of the victory he obtained against Maxence at Ponte Molle on the Tiber about 2 miles from Rome.[119] It consists of 3 arches ornamented by eight fluted columns of the corinthian order eight statues and many bas-reliefs.

The elevation of the Roman soil appears here and throughout the whole of the Forum or Campo Vaccino[120] very considerable. It had incroached so much upon this arch that above 12 feet of it were under ground until the year 1804 when by order of Pope Pius VII the earth

---

118   flat surface - the word was already archaic.
119   Constantine, Emperor AD 306-337. The Arch of Constantine was erected to commemorate his victory over his rival Maxentius in AD 312 in a battle near the Milvian Bridge (Ponte Molle). thus establishing Constantine's position as Emperor in the West.
120   The Cow Field, used as such at least until the nineteenth century, was on the site of the Roman Forum.

around was taken away and the base of the arch and the antient triumphal way laid open.

The same work was also performed at the same time to the arch of Severus[121] (Arco di Settimo Severo) which was equally or indeed more inclosed and hidden by the earth. This arch is situated at the foot of the Capitol and was erected in the year 205 A.D. in honor of Severus and Carracalla[122] his son for victories obtained against the Parthians and other barbarous nations. It is built of marble contains three openings and is decorated by eight corinthian fluted columns and various sculptures of but little merit. In one side there is a door and staircase which leads to the upper part where formerly was placed the statues of the Emperor and his two sons in a chariot of bronze.

At the end of the Campo Vaccino near the Coliseum is the Arch of Titus erected by the Senate and people of Rome after the conquest of Jerusalem. It is of white marble and of a single arch but for the beauty of its architecture and sculpture not inferior to any of them. It was formerly ornamented by eight fluted columns of the composite order but only four of these remain. The interior of the Arch is ornamented with sculptures of great beauty but much damaged and broken. In the middle of the vaults is the apotheosis of the Emperor in the middle of sculptured rosettes. On each side is a bas-relief - one representing Titus in the triumphal chariot & the other various spoils and prisoners of Jerusalem.

After breakfast I went with Sir H. Davy to the Academy del' Lincei[123] to make some experiments on different charcoals but in two experiments the globes burst and the results were lost.

S. 16. Repeated to day the experiments of yesterday in stronger vessels and burned the charcoals of turpentine and alcohol obtained by sulphuric acid and common charcoal in oxygen. The object was to ascertain if any water were formed and in all the experiments it appeared evident being most plentiful with the charcoal of Alcohol and least with the charcoal of turpentine. All these charcoals are conductors of electricity and it is probable that they owe that power and their black colour to hydrogen the diamond being pure carbon.

S. 17. Went to day to the Palace of Monti Cavallo[124] situated on the summit of Mont Quirinale[125]. Before the palace is a large place ornamented by an egyptian obelisque of red granite 45 feet in height

---

121   Septimius Severus, Emperor AD 193-211.
122   M. Aurelius Antoninus, nicknamed Caracalla, Emperor AD 211-217.
123   Accademia del Lincei.
124   The Palazzo del Quirinale, begun in 1574 and lived in by several Popes until it was taken over by King Victor Emmanuel in 1870. It has remained the residence of the Italian Head of State ever since.
125   Monte Quirinale was one of the seven hills of Rome.

without the pedestal and formerly belonging to the Mausoleum of Augustus. On each side of the obelisque is a group one representing Castor and his horse and the other Pollux and his courser at least that is the current story and they are ascribed to Phidias and Praxatiles[126]. The figures are 17 feet in height and were brought I believe by Constantine the great from Alexandria to Rome to ornament his baths.

The Palace is the most pleasantly situated of any in Rome and gives a fine view of the city. The interior is interesting at this moment for its unfinished state. It was intended for the palace of the intended king of Rome son of Napoleon the first. The apartments in which the works of ornament and luxury have been commenced are numerous and the designs extremely appropriate and beautiful. Antient columns of beautiful materials have been cut up to form the fire places and the entrances; and the ceiling of each chamber contains a beautiful painting. The design on the ceiling of the chamber intended for the Emperor represented night[;] a bard was sleeping over his harp and dreams of war conquest and glory hovering around him; the idea and the execution were beautiful but the application not very felicitous. Mosaic work both in wood and stone abounded and no expence has indeed been spared in the commencement of these works. - The place was shewn us where the Pope was taken prisoner and the door and staircase by which the soldiers entered.[127]

From this place we went to the Villa Borghese and passed a pleasant hour in the gardens which abound with fountains temples and statues.

I hardly know why I endeavour to describe the antiquities and works of art that I see in the course of my walks. I know very well I can give no idea of their beauty or value and that the observations I make would appear absurd to others but this journal is not intended to instruct and inform or to convey even an imperfect idea of what it speaks of: its sole use is to recal to my mind at some future time the things I see now and the most effectual way to do that will be I conceive to write down be they good or bad or however imperfect my present impressions.

In the evening a dispute occurred in the street opposite to the house in which we reside between two Neapolitan soldiers during the quarrel one received from the other four or five stabs in the stomach made with a long knife. They all went off to the hall of justice.

M. 18. Nothing particular.

T. 19. To day a long walk from 9 o clk till ½ past 4. I took a description of Rome with me and first ascended the Column of

---

126   The attribution to Phidias and Praxiteles is no longer accepted. The statues are now
       identified as Roman copies of Greek originals. Because of the statues this hill was
       also sometimes called Monte Cavallo.
127   See note on 6 February 1814.

Antoninus to trace out from it the rout I wished to go. - From thence proceeding to Piazza di Pietro[128] I came to the Custom house or Douane de Terre[129] in front of which appear the remains of a temple supposed to be erected to Antoninus Pius. The remains consist of 11 columns of immense size surmounted by a grand entablature. They are formed of greek marble and are 39½ feet in height and 4 feet 2 inches in diameter at the base. They are of the corinthian order and fluted but much broken and defaced.

Passing on to the Church of Jesus[130] I entered to see the Chapel of S[t]. Ignace[131] which is remarkable for the quantity of lapis lazula employed in its decoration. The church is considered as one of the richest in Rome and is ornamented by gilding and painting to an extraordinary degree. The pavement is decorated by large mosaic work and the various chapels on each side abound with marbles sculptures and paintings. The Chapel of St Ignace is one of the richest in Rome. It is ornamented by 4 large columns covered with lapis lazula and fluted by ribs of Bronze doré on each side of the Chapel is a fine group in marble one representing Faith adored by all nations and the other the triumph of religion. In the front of the chapel is a group representing the Trinity and a globe which is in the hand of the Father is a piece of pure lapis lazula nearly 12 inches in diameter. There are also various sculptures and bas-reliefs of bronze doré and some fine chandeliers.

From this church the road is strait to the Capitol. It is situated on the summit of the Mount of the same name which is ascended at this day by a grand staircase or ascent of little inclination conducting to the opening on the summit no[w] called Piazza del Campidoglio. Here on the site of the former Capitol are erected three Palaces before which are placed various antique statues and amongst them the equestrian figure of Marcus Aurelius Antoninus of bronze doré. It was found in the Forum or Campo Vaccino and is the only equestrian statue that remains of the old city of Rome. The air and energy of the horse is wonderful: it is considered as the most perfect work of the kind.

The two side Palaces are appropriated to the purpose of a museum and contain many antiquities. I merely passed into the court my object being to see the larger remains of Rome. Accordingly I passed on to the Forum and came to the remains of Il Tempio di Giove Tonnante[132]. This temple was erected by the Emperor Augustus to Jupiter as an acknowledgement of support received in time of necessity. The part

---

128 Piazza di Pietra.
129 The Custom House (Dogana) incorporated part of the temple erected by Antoninus Pius (Emperor AD 138-161) in honour of Hadrian in AD 145. It is now the Roman Stock Exchange.
130 The Gesù - the Jesuit Church.
131 The tomb of St. Ignatius Loyola, founder of the Jesuit Order.
132 The Temple of Jupiter Tonans (Jupiter the Thunderer) was built in 22 BC. However, the columns which Faraday saw are those of the Temple of Vespasian (Emperor AD 69-79), built in AD 81.

remaining consists of three fluted columns of the corinthian order supporting a massive piece of the entablature beautifully sculptured and having on it part of the antient inscription. 'Till lately only a part of these remains could be seen the earth having covered the lower portion at present the whole is uncovered and the beauty of the proportions perceived.

Close to this temple are eight large columns of oriental granite 40 feet high and 12 feet in circumference at the base. They are the remains of a building called at present the Temple of Concord[133] and supposed to have been erected in commemoration of the harmony existing in the family of Augustus. The part which remains formed the portic[o] of the building. The columns are Ionic and five of them are single pieces of granite.

These remains are not many steps from the Arch of Severus on the opposite side of which is a small church erected on and formed out of the ruins of the prison Mamertine in which place according to tradition Peter the Apostle was detained nine months in the time of Nero[134]. I could find no person to give me admission.

Advancing towards the Coliseum I came to a building easily recognised to be antient from its present state its structure and its materials. This was the temple of Antoninus & Faustine[135] erected 168 A.D. to this Emperor and his wife by the Roman Senate. - The part now remaining is the two side walls, the columns of the portico and the entablature. The columns are ten in number of the Corinthian order very large and each of a single piece of Marble antiently called Lapis Caristius. Their whole height is 43 feet the circumference of the shaft below 12 feet. The entablature is richly sculptured with figures and ornaments and is of white greek marble. A church has been built within the walls called after St Laurent.

Next came the Temple of Remus[136] and afterwards three large arches appeared composed of brick and before them many ruins. These are the remains of the temple of Peace[137] erected by Vespasian in the year 77 A.D. This edifice appears to have been very large and must have covered much ground. The three arches formed one of the sides of the building and the ruins that lye about indicate the position of the opposite arches and the width of the space between them. Many fragments of the sculptures that formerly decorated the building are found at times on the

---

133   Now identified not as the Temple of Concord but the Temple of Saturn, rebuilt after
       a fire in the fourth century   (the Temple of Concord, dedicated in 367 BC,
       commemorated the concord between the patricians and plebeians and was adjacent
       to the Temple of Vespasian).
134   Emperor AD 54-68.
135   Faustina.
136   Temple of Romulus, said to have been dedicated by the Emperor Maxentius to his
       son of that name who died as a child.
137   Now identified as the Basilica of Maxentius, begun between AD 306 and 312 and
       later completed by Constantine.

spot. The vault of the nave was originally supported by eight beautiful white marble columns. One was found in the ruins in the time of Pope Paul Vth and now stands before the church of Santa Marie Magiore[138] having an image of the Virgin on the summit. It is a beautiful object. The width of this temple is supposed to have been 202 feet and its length 302 feet.

On advancing from this temple towards the Ampitheatre the remains of a building are seen which like the opinions formed respecting them look different ways. They consist of two arches or alcoves one facing the north and the other the south and an enormously thick wall, the whole of brick. The opinion of some antiquaries is that they were temples dedicated to Venus and to Rome but the more general opinion is that they were devoted to the Sun and Moon[139].

Taking a road leading towards the other side of the forum I came to the ruins of the Palace of the Caesars. I saw them but imperfectly for they are mostly among gardens and grounds which are now private property. Returning and passing along the other side of the Campo Vaccino I arrived at Il Tempio di Giove Statore[140] as it is generally called though opinions differ much as to the original intention of the building. There are three fluted corinthian columns of grecian marble and they are supposed to be part of a lateral range the diameter of each is 4½ feet and the height 45 feet. A portion of an entablature of beautiful workmanship still remains upon them.

At a little distance stands a single fluted marble column 44 feet in height. It is assigned to different deities.[141]

Nearly in the middle of the Campo Vaccino is a fountain with two simple jets of water which fall from a lateral erection into a very large bason being 76 feet in circumference and formed entirely of oriental granite.[142] It is in one piece. It is supported on a foot and is similar in form to a depressed urn. It is of antient origine and was found with the colossal statue of Marphore near the arch of Settimius Severus.[143]

Passing from thence to the Coliseum I after a while went towards the walls of the city and arrived at the Place of S^t. Giovanni di [   ][144] one of the largest and finest in Rome. This place is ornamented by an

---

138   Basilica of Santa Maria Maggiore. The column was brought from the Basilica of Maxentius by Pope Paul V (r.1605-21).

139   Temple of Venus and Rome, designed as a single temple by the Emperor Hadrian and dedicated in AD 135. Once the largest temple in Rome, its double sanctuaries were placed back to back.

140   Now identified as the Temple of Castor and Pollux, restored by Augustus in 6 BC.

141   Column of Phocas, erected in AD 608. Its identifying inscription was uncovered in 1813, during excavations financed by the Duchess of Devonshire. This was presumably too recent to have been noted in Faraday's guidebook.

142   Probably the Fountain of Juturna, the principal fountain in classical Rome around which the citizens gathered to hear the latest news and drink the supposedly curative waters.

143   Septimius Severus.

144   Piazza di San Giovanni in Laterano.

Egyptian obelisk which was first erected at Thebes by Ramesis king of Egypt above 3000 years ago and was dedicated to the Sun.[145] Constantine the great brought it from the ruins of that city and conveyed it to Alexandria with the intention of transporting it to and erecting it at Constantinople but his death occurring his son Constance brought it to Rome and erected it in the middle of the great Circus. It was Sixtus Vth who in later days raised it from out of the ground and finding it broken into three pieces reunited it and erected it in this place under the direction of the Chevalier Fontana.

This obelisk is of red granite is 99 feet high without the base and 9 feet square at the lower part. It is covered with hieroglyphics. At the bottom is a statue of S[t] John and a fountain supplying water to the Environs. In this Place are also some fine modern buildings as the grand Palace given by Constantine the great to Pope S[t] Sylvestre[146] the Church of S[t] John or the Baptistery and the Basilique di S[t] Giovanni di Laterenze.[147] This Church is the first and the principle temple of Rome and according to the Catholics of the Catholic world. It is a magnificent piece of Architecture and within abounds in riches paintings and statues. The chapels are extremely rich more particularly that called corsini in which are fine columns paintings and sculptures and a beautiful mosaic representing S[t] Andrea Corsini copied from Guido Reni. Above the grand altar within a gothic tabernacle is guarded with great care (according to my informer) the heads of S[t] Peter and S[t] Paul.

Nearly opposite to this church is a smaller building but claiming and receiving more respect. It is called Santa scala or the holy steps sometimes the Chapel of the most holy saviour or the Sanctum sanctorum. This place was built by Sixtus 5th and consists of a magnificent portico and five flights of steps. The middle series are those termed holy. They are 28 in number of white marble and are said to be those which belonged to the Palace of Pilate at Jerusalem whence they were brought to Rome. These steps having been sanctified by the blood of Jesus Christ who passed over them several times are held in great veneration by all devout persons who to express it mount them on their knees saying prayers the while and descend again by the lateral steps. These stairs were much worn by the numbers who ascended but in order to prevent their further destruction Clement 12th[148] covered them with thick planks of walnut tree wood which when worn out are replaced by new ones. On the altar at the summit of the steps is an image of the Saviour 5 feet in height which according to an antient tradition was begun by S[t] Luke and finished by Angels. Such is the account I received from a really

---

145   The obelisk was erected by Thothmes IV in front of the Temple of Ammon at Thebes
       (15th century BC) and brought to Rome by Constantine II in 337.
146   Pope St Sylvester I.
147   Battistero and Basilica di San Giovanni in Laterano.
148   Pope 1730-40.

intelligent Roman. On the left hand of the building are some fine mosaics full of gilding.

The view is interrupted from this place by the intervention of the antient walls of Rome erected by the Emperor Aurelian[149] and close at hand is the Porte di St Giovanno.[150] In a garden before the church are the ruins of Nero's aqueduct. It was erected to conduct the waters of Claudien[151] to Mount Coelius.

Passing onwards along the side of the wall I came to the Church of the Cross of Jerusalem[152] near to which in a vineyard are the remains of a temple dedicated to Venus and Cupid but of which I had a very imperfect view. In the same vineyard is another part of the aqueduct of Nero which was formerly continued to the walls of the city joining them at the adjacent Porto Magiore[153] and being then carried on by the walls. In another vineyard close at hand are the remains of L'Ampitheatre Castrense.[154] - This building wholly of brick forms at present part of the walls of the city but it is necessary in order to see it properly to pass out at St John's Gate and for that I had not time. I went on therefore to Porta Magiore.

This porte was formerly part of the aqueduct of Tiberius Claudius[155] but being the part under which passed the public road it was formed in a more magnificent and imposing manner than the other arches. When Aurelian extended the walls this edifice was taken in as a part of the fortifications with part of the aqueduct and it now forms one of the city gates. There are three inscriptions on this building indicating & commemorating the various restitutions that had been made at different times. - This aqueduct conveyed the water from two different sources in separate canals to Rome. The gate is built with large blocks of limestone put together without cement. On passing under the arch you see in the distance the aqueduct which conveys the waters Julie Tipula[156] and Marcie to Mont Esquilin[157]. It passes the walls by Porte St Laurent.[158]

Proceeding straight from this gate into the city the eye is caught by the ruins of a dome or vault in a vineyard on the right hand. They are

---

149   Aurelian, Emperor AD 270-275.
150   Porta San Giovanni.
151   Or may read Claudian. The Aqua Claudia, begun by Caligula, Emperor AD 37-40, was completed by Claudius, Emperor AD 41-59, Nero's predecessor, to bring water to the Caelian Hill, now the Lateran.
152   Santa Croce in Gerusalemme.
153   Porta Maggiore.
154   Amphitheatrum Castrense.
155   The Emperor Claudius, see note 142.
156   The Aqua Julia Tepula was 15½ miles long; 6½ miles of it were on the same arches as the Marcia.
157   The Esquiline was another of the seven hills of Rome. The Aqua Marcia, built 144-143 BC, the first high-level aqueduct, was over 60 miles long.
158   Porta San Lorenzo.

the remains of a temple erected to Minerva Medici[159] or the goddess of health. It is of brick and of a diagonal form. Farther on were the ruins of the Chateau de l'eau Julie[160] commonly called the trophies of Marcus[161] because here were found the two marble trophies which at this day adorn the Capitol. These ruins consist of enormous brick walls and arches of considerable height but little extent. It is supposed to have been a place destined to receive and distribute the waters of the spring Julie.

Passing round these ruins another road appears which lead me towards Porte S[t] Laurent. On the summit of this gate are the ruins of the triple aqueduct before mentioned.

I did not go to the gate but turning off from the ruins of Chateau de l'eau &c I arrived at the Arch of Gallien[162] erected in the year 260 and dedicated to Gallien and Salonine his wife by a private person Marc Aureli Victor[;] at present there remains but a small part of the arch i.e. two pilasters and the entablature[;] formerly there were six pilasters and two small arches on the sides of the grand & central one. The architecture is common and there is little striking in its appearance except its air of antienty.

From hence I proceeded to the Place of S[t] Marie Magiore[163] in the middle of which as I have before observed is erected on a noble pedestal the grand and magnificent column found at the temple of Peace. It is 58½ feet high and 20 feet 3 inches in circumference. The interior of the church is very rich especially the chapel of the Virgin which is decorated by four fluted columns of antient jasper supporting an entablature the frieze of which is agate. In the midst of a field of lapis lazula is placed the picture of the virgin done (says tradition) by S[t] Luke. It is surrounded by precious stones and supported by four angels of Bronze d'ore.

Passing out of the church behind the altar I came into an open place where stands another Egyptian obelisk which with that no[w] on Monte Cavallo[164] were found before the Mausoleum of Augustus. They were brought by the Emperor Claudius from Egypt to Rome. The one here is of red granite and 43 feet high without the base.

---

159   Minerva Medica.
160   Castellum Aquae Juliae (Tepulae). The 'castellum' was the basin or tank from which the water was distributed to individual destinations.
161   Trophies of Marius - marble panoplies now on the balustrade of Piazza de Campidoglio.
162   Arch of Gallienus, the middle arch of a triple gate erected at the time of Augustus and dedicated in AD 262 in honour of Gallienus and his consort Salonina, a Christian, by the city prefect M. Aurelius Victor.
163   Piazza di Santa Maria Maggiore.
164   The other obelisk is actually in the Piazza dell'Esquilino.

From this spot I came by various streets to the baths of Titus[165] an edifice calculated to give an astonishing idea of Roman grandeur luxury and effort. My humble information relating to them runs thus. The greeks were the first who gave the example to the asiatics of the use of baths. The Romans in imitation of them introduced them at Rome and for that purpose built those places called Therma[166] a word derived from the greek and signifying hot places. These were divided into an infinite number of vaulted chambers in some of them were warm waters in other odoriferous waters destined to be used as baths. In others were hot vapours to heat the body during the winter with apartments where it was rubbed with oils and perfumed. There were also separate places destined for the use of females. These therma inclosed temples perystiles games, the schools of philosophers, libraries, theatres alleys arbours &c indeed every thing that the arts could contribute to their magnificence their convenience or their luxury. There were also places appropriated to the games of the discs the pugilist and the course. There were at Rome twelve public baths or therma and 860 were counted which were private. In the reign of Nero their number was almost infinite.

Though the baths of Titus were not so large as those of Diocletian[167] or Carracalla yet as the fine arts flourished most at the time when they were erected they were more esteemed both for the superiority of the Architecture and the ornaments. They surpassed also in richness and taste those of Agrippa and Nero raised at later periods. This edifice had two stages. The lower was appropriated to be used as baths and the upper destined for exercises most noble for the mind and most salutary for the body. There are seven vast corridors or galleries on the lower stage and it is by one of them that entrance is now gained to the chambers of the baths. These are in number thirty six all painted in arabesque with small tables on which are to be seen charming and graceful figures. Time moisture &c have done great injury so that little of these paintings remain at present to be seen.

These chambers having been filled and covered with earth by the motions which have taken place in the soil of Rome they were for many ages hidden but were discovered and opened in the time of Raphael and according to some by Raphael himself. After a time they were again filled with earth and remained so untill 1776 when they were again in part cleared out. 'Till lately it was difficult to penetrate into the interior of this edifice and by the light of torches to view the paintings which have escaped destruction but latterly works have been commenced and still continue with much vigour to clear out all the chambers and galleries that easy access may be had to this interesting relict of former times. -

---

165   Very little remains of the Baths of Titus (Emperor 79-81). Faraday probably refers to the ruins of the Baths of Trajan (Emperor AD 98-117) nearby, of which some of the central hall and outer wall remain.
166   Thermae.
167   Emperor AD 284-305.

I entered with a guide who carried some torches and passed through various large and small apartments in the lower range. The whole edifice appears to be of brick but it was formerly covered on the sides and roof with plaister and painted and on the ground with marbles and mosaic work. In one chamber was a cavity in the wall in which was found a considerable quantity of old roman coin at present deposited in the Museum of the Vatican. On the sides and roofs of some apartments entirely under ground the original ornaments still remained though much injured. They were paintings of small figures & various implements of industry and war. In one of the small outer chambers is deposited all the pieces of antient work found in clearing out the earth. It contains fragments of marble sculptures mosaic work glass &c but with no arrangement.

At a little distance from this place are the ruins of a building called the seven chambers which is supposed to have the reservoir of water belonging to the baths. They are in the middle of a vineyard and I could find no person to conduct me there. On another side of the baths are some circular ruins called the Imperial Palace and supposed to have been built by Titus. It was here that the famous group of the Laocoon was found and also many other statues and marbles.[168]

These baths were restored and enlarged by the Emperor Trajan and hence were named after him. They stand on the ground which formed the gardens of Mecaenas[169] and close to the palaces of Horace & Virgil[170] and the tower from whence Nero beheld the burning of Rome.[171]

Leaving these baths I arrived after much winding at the Piazza Termini which is ornamented by a fine fountain supplied by the waters of Felix.[172] This fountain was constructed by Pope Sixtus the fifth & consists of three arcades each finely sculptured. The middle one represents Moses bringing water from the rock a grand and colossal figure; in one of the side arches is sculptured Aaron leading the people to drink at this miraculous stream and in the other is depicted Gideon selecting his soldiers from the army by their attitudes at the river's brink.

---

168   The Laocoön was discovered in 1506 near the ruins of Nero's Golden House, the Domus Aurea, which was overlaid by the Baths of Trajan.
169   C. Cilnius Maecenas was a wealthy landowner, patron of the arts, and confidential adviser to Augustus.
170   The poets Vergil (70-19 BC) and Horace (65-8 BC) were members of Maecenas' literary circle. Vergil had a house near the Gardens of Maecenas, and Horace may have done as well.
171   The Torre delle Milizie (actually a thirteenth century building) was traditionally known as the Torre di Nerone and identified as the place where Nero 'fiddled while Rome burned' during the great fire of AD 64. It is near Trajan's Forum and cannot be the one meant here. Nero's palace, the Domus Aurea, built after the fire, was in this area. His earlier residence, which was destroyed, was the Domus Transitoria on the Palatine Hill.
172   The Fontana dell' Acqua Felice, built in 1587 and named after Pope Sixtus V (Felice Peretti), now stands in the Piazza San Bernardo.

The basin which receives the waters is ornamented by four lions two of these are egyptian and of basalt and their pedestals are sculptured with hyeroglyphics, the other two are of greek marble and workmanship.
Close at hand are the baths of Dioclesian[173] the largest that were erected. I have not yet seen them or the churches that have been formed in some of the apartments but turning off took my road home hungry thirsty and fatigued.

W. 20th. Set off this morning at 8 o.clk in another direction with the hopes of making the day as interesting as yesterday and was not disappointed. I went first to the Pantheon a work esteemed as much for its beauty and perfection as for its origin and preservation. This superb temple was erected in the year 727 of Rome and 24 years before the commencement of the Christian Era by Marc Agrippa and was improved and restored at later periods by other Emperors.[174] It was dedicated by Agrippa to Jupiter the Avenger but as the statues of other gods were also found there it has obtained the name of the Pantheon. This edifice is circular; its interior diameter is 132 feet and the walls are 19 feet in thickness. Its height is the same as its diameter. It is covered by a dome of stone in which is a central opening 26 feet wide by which light is admitted to the interior of the building. There are three grand recesses formed in the thickness of the wall in which statues were formerly placed at present they contain chapels of great beauty and in smaller niches between them are found smaller chapels. A series of large columns run round the interior and support a finely sculptured frieze. From behind this frieze the dome rises formed into pannels which formerly were covered with silver or bronze d'ore. The portico before the building is of enormous size and majesty it is 103 feet in length and projects forward from the rotunda 61 feet. Its columns are 16 in number each formed of a single piece of granite 14 feet in circumference and 38 in height. This portico was formerly covered with bronze but the metal has been removed and applied to other uses. What remained in the time of Urban 8th was taken by that Pope and applied in the construction of the grand temple in S[t] Peters. It is said that the nails only weighed 9374 lbs and that the whole weight of the bronze was 450280 lbs. The walls of the Portico are covered with marbles and sculpture.

Before this building is an open space now used as a market in which is a pretty fountain and on it is erected a small egyptian obelisk of granite covered with hieroglyphics.[175]

---

173   Baths of Diocletian, Emperor AD 284-305.
174   The Pantheon was originally a temple built by Agrippa, the son-in-law of Augustus in 27 BC. It was damaged by fire in AD 80, and restored by Domitian, but was rebuilt in brick between ca AD 118-129, by Hadrian, Emperor 117-138.
175   The fountain was set up by Giacomo della Porta in 1578; in 1711 Pope Clement XI added the obelisk dating from the 6th century BC.

From thence I was conducted partly by chance partly by favour to the Teâtro di Marcello erected by Octavian Augustus and dedicated by him to his nephew Marcelles the son of his sister Octavius.[176] At present it appears as part of a circular series of columns and arches between and within which appear dirty houses and noisy shops, it forms indeed one side of a street. The architecture of this theatre is considered as being of the most perfect kind and the parts which remain are taken as models by modern artists. It formerly consisted of four tier of the different orders of architecture but the upper two are entirely ruined. It was 367 feet in diameter and capable of containing 30000 spectators. 600 wild beasts were slain there on the day of dedication.

Leaving the theatre I found after much search the arch of Giano Quadrifronti[177] a building very different to the one I expected and which could not readily excite in the mind of an ignorant person any idea of the use for which it was intended. This arch is one of those called Jani which were erected in various parts of the antient city as shelters for the people either from the sun or rain. The present is the only one remaining at this day and takes its title of quadrifronti from the similarity of all its faces. It is square in form and open on all sides each face is ornamented on the lower part by 12 niches and above in various openings. The lower part is composed entirely of Greek marble in enormous blocks but brick work appears above. This however is the work of a later period and was intended to convert the building into a place of defense.

Very near to this Arch is seen a smaller one built with marble and erected to the Emperor Severus [   ][178] by the various merchants of the Forum Boarium[179] which existed in this place. It is small and covered with sculptures which are not much esteemed and have been greatly injured by time. The opening is square. It is perhaps 12 or 14 feet high certainly not much more.

Taking a path opposite the small arch which has been formed by the feet of the curious I came in sight of the Cloaca Maxima or large subterranean vault by which the waters of the city were conveyed into the Tiber. These vaults were first formed by Tarquin the antient[180] and are arranged as our sewers with larger and smaller branches gathering from every quarter. This grand cloaca is a work fitted to excite admiration both for its size and solidity though its appearance this day is not so striking as formerly part of the antient stone work being hidden by a brick wall and the cloaca itself being three parts filled with mud and

176   Marcellus and Octavia.
177   Janus Quadrifrons.
178   Arco degli Argentari, built in AD 204, portrayed the two sons of Septimius Severus.
179   The ancient Roman cattle market, now partly occupied by the Piazza della Bocca della Verità.
180   Tarquinius Priscus, King of Rome c.616-579 BC. The Cloaca Maxima is also attributed to Tarquinius Superbus (r. ca 534-510 BC), the last king of Rome. It was not arched over until about 200 BC.

earth. It is constructed with three tiers of enormous blocks of stone laid together without cement each block is 5 feet long and nearly 3 in thickness: the arch was formerly 12 feet high and as many wide but the space is at present much smaller. The length of this part is above 300 feet. Near to it are the remains of other cloaca which were formerly connected with the great one and water is running through them all.

On taking the great road which leads towards the walls of the city I came in sight of the ruins of the Grand Circus called the Circus Maximus the largest of all that were erected by the Romans and the history of which is the most varied and the most important. This Circus was built by Tarquin[181] and according to the popular description was 2008 feet long and 879 wide. It was capable of containing 150000 persons. Julius Caesar repaired and augmented it with great magnificence and according to Pliny made it sufficiently large to accomodate 260000 persons. Afterwards Augustus erected in the centre of it the obelisk which is seen at this day in the Piazza del Popolo. Having been destroyed in the time of Nero by fire Trajan re erected it with an increase of magnificence and of such dimensions that it could contain 380000 persons. Lastly it was repaired and embellished by Constantine the Great who placed in the middle of it the obelisk which now stands in the Place of St John.[182]

At present there remains nothing of this mighty building but some masses of bricks and ruined arches on which are formed gardens and vineyards.

Still further in advance I found the ruins of the Terme di Caracalla. These occupy a large extent of ground and consist of various large saloons and chambers inclosed within a high and massive wall. Formerly they were classed with respect to size between those of Diocletian and Titus exceeding the latter but not equalling the former. The ruins however are more open and spacious than those of any similar edifice. This building was formerly one of the most magnificent of its kind it consisted of two stages the lower being as usual appropriated to the bathers and the upper to the various athletic games and exercises. The upper one can be best examined for except in a few places the lower is entirely inclosed and filled by the earth. Those which remain above ground are numerous and some of extraordinary magnitude. One chamber is 188 feet long and 134 wide and was covered in by a flat roof which was supported by bars and grates of bronze and copper. This roof was considered by antient architects as a wonder in art because of its size and level form both of which increased the difficulty of supporting it. Many of the most valued antient sculptures and riches have been found here which are now deposited in various museums and repositories.

---

181   The Circus was said to have been built originally about 600 BC by Tarquinius Priscus.
182   Piazzadi San Giovanni in Laterano.

Advancing toward the gate of the city I came to the door of a vineyard bearing the words <u>Sepolcra Scipionum</u>[183] indicating the ruins it contained. I did not enter to view the Tomb of the Scipios but it appeared from the road to be a round ruined edifice partly enclosed by huts and cottages.

Before arriving at the Gate the road passes under an Arch erected by the Senate of Rome in honor of the Emperor Nero Claudius Drusus.[184] The architecture is plain but solid; it has formerly constituted part of an aqueduct and is supposed to have conducted the waters of Marcie[185] which were the best about Rome to the Baths of Caracalla.

This gate of the City is named after St Lorenzo[186] and opens on the celebrated Appian way one of the most magnificent roads of antient Rome both for its excellence and its ornaments. The latter consisted of various tombs temples and other buildings. The remains of these works are very plentiful and very interesting. I rambled along

[The manuscript breaks off at this point]

---

183   The Scipios, a distinguished military family in Republican Rome, flourished in the second and third centuries BC. The Scipio tomb was discovered in 1780.
184   The Arch was erected neither in honour of Drusus, the younger brother of the Emperor Tiberius (r. AD 14-37), nor Nero, but dates from the second century AD.
185   Aqua Marcia.
186   Not the Porta San Lorenzo but the Porta San Sebastiano, originally the Porta Appia.

Faraday to Benjamin Abbott[187]

Rome, May 1, 1814

Dear Ben,

It was with much pleasure that I began a correspondence with you nor was the feeling diminished at any time during its continuance and though at present the interest between us is much greater than it was before which necessarily will render the progress of our epistolary communication much slower yet it is not at all my intention to drop it & I am in hopes that as it becomes more tardy in its advancement it will also become more important more instructive & more interesting. Certainly I cannot now advance in excuse for the uninteresting strain of my letters a want of matter for every day presents sufficient to fill a book. As I hope & expect that the good understanding still continues between our family & yours I expect that when they get a letter in Weymouth Street[188] you will hear that I have thought on you. I shall therefore fill this paper principally with philosophical matter & as far as my feeble powers will permit me will endeavour to make it interesting. I have commenced it this 1st day of May 1814 in the Ancient city of Rome & hope to send it off on Wednesday by favour to England but if it cannot go then I shall keep it by me & add to it as to a journal & send it when an opportunity occurs and opportunities I hope will now be frequent.

Here the thing which is uppermost in the mind of every person is the strange chain of events which have brought about the downfall of Napoleon the Great (the title he had taken) & of the system of government that he had established these events are so singular & have occured with such rapidity that it appears as a waking dream passing rapidly over the mind & of which it is difficult to form an idea of reality. To see the Bourbons on the throne of France was never expected & though a universal European peace was earnestly desired no hopes of it were entertained at present those events appear close at hand. God grant they may come to pass. Amongst these occurrences England has shone out most conspicuously & her firm & steady virtue & constancy are held up to the whole world as a model worthy of imitation & England meets with her due in the praises of every one. In France I found every one loved the English at Paris they all praise the English & Since we have left the French dominions we have been received with testimonies of pleasure & gratitude as strong as it was possible for the tongue to express. At Lucca we found the whole population without the gates waiting for the English it was said that the Army which had debarked at Leghorn

---

187   MS letter in IEE Archives, also in LPW and BJ pp.128-130.
188   Faraday's family home.

would enter Lucca that day & the inhabitants had come out to receive them as brothers the town was decorated in the most brilliant manner by colours drapery & embroidery flying from every window & in the evening general illuminations took place done as expressions of their joy at their deliverance from the french government & the English were hailed every where as their Saviours.

                                                    Geneva   July 24, 1814.
     This morsel of paper dear Ben has made a longer journey than that I intended for it - and instead of being in London it is now at Geneva but I hope that it will not be long before it is at its original destination and procuring me the pleasure of a letter from you. On perusing the last (and the first) page I found the matter so different from that at present in my head that I was suddenly urged to destroy it but second thoughts induced me to leave it unaltered since it conveyed the ideas of that moment which to you will not be more uninteresting than those of the present. As it is my intention to well fill this paper I shall write it as much in the style of description as in that of a letter or rather I shall write it as my thoughts run too much indeed out of order. You will find in this letter not a regular description of my journey but a few observations on those things which I have found most remarkable and which have been most under my notice for as all parts of my travels have pleased me it will be useless to say I liked Aix or I like Nice &c. It is now 9 months ago since I left London but I have not forgot and never shall forget the ideas that were forced on my mind in the first days to me who had lived all my days of remembrance in London in a city surrounded by a flat green country a hill was a mountain and a stone a rock for though I had abstract ideas of the things and could say rock & mountain and could talk of them yet I had no perfect ideas, conceive then the astonishment the pleasure and the information, that entered my mind in the varied county of Devonshire w[h]ere the foundations of the earth were first exposed to my view and where I first saw granite limestone &c in those places and those forms where the ever working and all wonderful hand of nature had placed them. No Ben, it is impossible you can conceive my feelings and it is as impossible for me to describe them. The sea then presented a new scene of information and interest and on approaching the shore of France with what eagerness and how often were my eyes directed to the south. When arrived there I thought myself in an uncivilized country for never before or since have I seen such wretched beings as[?] at Morlaix. But I must break this train of thoughts Dear Ben and carry you in haste to Paris where art exerts her power to inform and astonish man. There are many things at Paris calculated in an eminent degree to arrest the progress of the traveller but these things consist in the works of men & I would rather talk to you of the works of nature however I must not forget to tell you of what I suppose you have heard at least, I earnestly hope so namely <u>Iodine</u> on which Sir H. Davy has made many experiments and he has written to the

Royal Society papers on the subject. This substance adds a fourth body to the class of supporters of combustion or to the class of undecomposed bodies attracted by the positive pole of the Voltaic apparatus and which by their strong and opposed attraction to other bodies produce light & heat and it is the only one of them which has been obtained in a separate pure & solid form. It is very heavy of a dark colour similar to plumbago and has much the appearance of that body when heated it melts and gives off or rises in the form of a beautifully coloured violet gas of great intensity and when cooled it appears in minute crystals but otherwise unchanged. It combines readily with many other bodies with all the metals except two that I have seen it tried on the two are Platinum & Gold and I have seen the compounds it forms with Iron Tin Lead Silver Mercury &c. It forms acids by combining with very different bodies thus Chlorine Hydrogen Phosphorus & Tin all form acid with it & possessing new & singular properties. It unites to Azote & like chlorine forms a detonating compound with it & with potassium sodium Baryum &c it forms substances very similar to the compounds of these bodies, with Chlorine indeed it resembles this body more than any other in its combinations. When added to Potash in solution two new compounds are formed one being [ ][189] binary compound of iodine & potassium similar to muriate of po[ ]h as it [ ] called and the other parallels with oxymuriate of potash for it contains all the oxygen of the alkali and detonates very readily with nitre. I am however but wasting time in writing that of which you have a complete account as far as it goes in England and shortly I suppose that Sir H - will send you further accounts for he works upon it every day. Before I leave iodine however I must ask you & also desire you to inform me of the state of your sentiments respecting chlorine whether you class that substance & fluorine with oxygene or whether you insulate the last body as in former times. On leaving Paris we visited Lyons rested at Montpellier for a few weeks and afterwds saw Aix Nice &c. Between Nice and Turin we crossed the Maritime alps by the Col de Tende in the month of Feby. not the most favourable season in the year for crossing these snowy mountains. The col de Tende cost us a day to cross it and at the summit we were elevated above 6000[feet] higher than the level of the sea. From Turin we went to Genoa where I first saw a torpedo and a water spout the torpedos here were small, too small for the experiments which Sir H.- wished to make with them these experiments were to ascertain whether the electric power of the torpedo could be made to decompose water. The apparatus used was that of Wollaston and the fluid solution of potassa[190] it being a very good conductor but though the animal gave several shocks which there is reason to suppose passed through the water yet no satisfactory result

---

189   Here and in the next line the original has been damaged by the seal. It probably
       read 'being a binary compound of iodine and potassium similar to muriate of
       potash as it is called'.
190   Presumably a potassium salt.

was obtained & no effect appeared to be produced. Sir H. has repeated these experiments since at Rimini with the torpedo of the adriatic Sea but they were also too small to give certain results. - Leaving Genoa we proceeded by water to Lereche and from thence to Florence a beautiful city where we remained some days here is a fine Museum of Natural History containing an immense quantity of things curious & instructive and some waxworks in anatomy & botany of the most delicate kind. The collection of apparatus is numerous and rendered invaluable by the instruments of Galileo & the Duke of Tuscany. The first telescope of Galileo & that with which he discovered the satellites of Jupiter is carefully preserved as an invaluable philosophical relic and also the first lens which he made which is set in a fine worked frame with an inscription it is cracked in two. There is also a vast quantity of electrical machines and apparatus. There is a machine of Red Velvet passing under a rubber of black silk & there is a collection of jars broken singularly by extraordinary explosions. Magnets here are numerous and very strong & there is a compound one which supports some Cwt[191]. Sir H took the opportunity whilst here of making many experiments on the diamond with the great lens of the Grand Duke, a noble instrument belonging to the academy and in these pursuits as in every other his attentive mind observed & demonstrated new facts. In the first experiment on the combustion of the diamond it was placed in the middle of a glass globe of 18 or 20 cubical inches capacity supported in a cradle of platinum fixed on a prop of the same metal the cradle was pierced full of holes to admit a free circulation of air ie oxygen for the globe was filled with the gas procured from hyperoxymuriate of potassa. On placing the apparatus thus arranged in the focus of the lens it, the diamond[192], shortly entered into combustion & on removing it from the instrument the combustion was observed to continue for above 4 minutes during this time the diamond gave off intense heat & a beautiful vivid scarlet light. It diminished rapidly in size and became at last a mere atom when it ceased to burn but on placing it again in the focus the whole rapidly disappeared the globe was found to contain nothing but a mixture of Carbonic and Oxygene gasses. This experiment was repeated several times and in all the cases the same striking phenomenon was observed, a phenomenon which lessens considerably the difference existing between diamond and charcoal. Sir H. burned also by the same instrument a piece of plumbago in oxygen and he heated also diamonds in Chlorine & Carbonic acid gasses but no change was produced, no compound no muriatic acid was formed in the first place and no carbonic oxide in the second. These experiments on carbonaceous substances were continued at Rome at which time charcoal obtained from Alcohol from Turpentine & from wood were weighed & burned; and from all these experiments it appeared

---

191   Cwt = hundredweight, about 50 kg.
192   The words 'the diamond' are an insertion, by Faraday, in the original.

that the diamond was pure crystallised carbon and that the black
compounds of carbon contained hydrogen though none of them in great
quantities plumbago also contained hydrogene and when heated in
chlorine the hydrogen was separated and fumes of muriatic acid clouded
the globe of the charcoals that obtained from turpentine by sulphuric
acid appeared the purest, then that from alcohol and lastly the charcoal
of wood[;] by purity I mean a want of hydrogen and the purest contained
the least hydrogen the charcoal of wood the most. Sir H- wrote an
account of these experiments which has been sent to the Royal Society &
I hope received – From Florence we went to Rome that City of Wonders.
but they are wonders created by a former nation & in a former age. You
know, Ben, my turn is not architectural nor though I can admire a
beautiful picture do I pretend to judge of it but certainly the things here
would affect any one and that mind must be dull indeed that is not urged
to think & think again on these astonishing remains of the Romans when
they appear in sight at every corner. I shall not pretend to describe them,
dear Ben, since descriptions far more perfect than those I can give you
are in England. The two things here most striking are the Coliseum & S^t
Peter's, and one is not more worthy of the ancients than the other is of
the moderns. The Coliseum is a mighty ruin & indeed so is Rome & so
are the Romans & it is almost impossible to conceive how the hardy
warlike race which conquered the globe has degenerated into modern
effeminate idle Italians. St Peter's appears to have been erected on the
plan of some fairy tale, for every luxury every ornament and every
embellishment & species of embellishment have been employed in its
erection. Its size is mighty it is mountaineous its architecture elegant its
materials costly they consist of Marbles of every hue & every kind
mosaics statues casts bronzes Jewels Gold & silver not spread[?] sparingly
but shiny & glittering in every part. The mosaics are numerous and large
and amongst the many designs that ornament this edifice there is but one
painted picture. – But I must for the present leave descriptions and
employ the rest of my paper on other matter which I have deferred to
the last because I wish it to remain clearest & strongest on your mind.
And in another letter I will give you such accounts of Naples, Vesuvius
&c. as I am able to do (the burning mountain I have been up twice, once
in the day time and once at night). As communications are so free
between this place & England, you will I hope not delay many days in
answering this letter the time of communication is I believe only 7 days,
and the letters must be franked reciprocally out of each country. You
will be so good as to let my Mother & friends know this and I hope I
shall hear from more than one person and by more than one letter. There
are two persons nearly strangers to my mother to which if you would
go[193] I should be much obliged. Mrs Greenwell[194] of the R. Institution

---

193   The words 'if you would go' were inserted by Faraday in the original.
194   Housekeeper at the Royal Institution.

to whom give my warmest thanks and remembrances for her kind
treatment of me when there and my warmest wishes for her prosperity
& happiness, & Mr Newman[195] of Lisle Street to whom I feel grateful for
his readiness in communicating to me such things as were useful &
instructive and whose success in life is I hope proportioned to his merits.
To my Mother & My brother you will of course go and you will say all
you can to them without any fear of outrunning the warmth of my
wishes. I have wrote many times to them & by such hands as I suppose
could not fail & I hope to hear now how they do & how affairs move.
Give them all for me[196] every warm feeling that can flow round the
heart. To Mr & Mrs Abbott & to your Brother & Sister I present my
respects & would if I durst my affections & to you, Dear Ben, I give the
dearest feeling that can enliven the days of man, friendship. May you
ever be happy & honorably so and may you never have cause to censure
the feelings of

          Your Friend,   M Faraday

Direct to Me at Geneva Post restaunt.

Faraday's Journal[197]

          Thursday, May 5th. - Went to-day to repeat an experiment first
made by Signor Morichini of Rome, on magnetism, and interesting in
the highest degree from its novelty and the important conclusions it leads
to.[198]
          The experiment consists in giving magnetism to a needle by the
solar rays, and was thus performed:- a needle was fixed on the point of
a pin of brass by a piece of wax, in a direction north and south nearly,
and a spectrum being formed by the decomposition of a strong ray of
white light, the violet rays were collected by a lens, and the focus
gradually drawn along the needle, beginning at the middle and
proceeding to the north point. A white screen was placed behind the
needle, which rendered it easy to bring the focus where it was wanted.
The focus was thus made to pass continually over the needle always in
the same direction, for an hour; and then the sun getting too high for our
apparatus, the experiment was finished for this day. On essaying the

---

195   Scientific instrument maker.
196   The words 'for me' were inserted by Faraday.
197   Journal text from here onwards is taken from BJ.
198   Domenico Pini Morichini (1773-1836) claimed to have magnetised a needle by
      drawing the violet rays of the solar spectrum along it. A connection between
      light and magnetism had long been sought, but neither Davy nor Faraday were
      convinced by Morichini. Faraday found a connection much later, when he
      showed that in a magnetic field polarised light changed its plane of polarisation.

needle by iron filings, and also by suspension, no effect was perceived. This was attributed to the misty air, for the sun was not so bright as it very often is here at this season. The result of the experiment when made successfully - that is, with a bright sun - is a magnetic needle, which points north and south, attracts iron filings, attracts the contrary pole of a common magnet, and repels the same pole, and possesses in every respect the same qualities. The experiment has been repeated above fifty times, and always with success - sometimes being completed in half an hour, and sometimes requiring the bright sun of two days. It is found that only the violet, the blue, and the green rays have this power - the violet most, and the green least. The red rays have been thrown in the same way on a needle at various times for twenty-four hours, but they produce no effect. The experiment also succeeds as well in winter as in summer, and in general is finished sooner. I saw one needle which had been thus formed. It was highly magnetic, attracted strongly iron, and quickly took its direction when suspended, observing the variation as other needles do. The needle which was taken for this experiment was reserved for another day, when the process would be continued.

Saturday, 7th. - Rose at twelve o'clock last night, and at two this morning was on the road to Naples. This early hour was chosen for the purpose of proceeding as far as possible on the first day, for, as the road is considered as very dangerous and abounding with robbers, it was necessary to take some precautions in order to ensure our arrival at Naples. At the second change of horses, six gendarmes joined us, and escorted us over a dangerous part of the road. At the next post the number was lessened, but some were with us all day. Ruins were plentiful in this day's journey, and two fine aqueducts appeared. The Colosseum, at the commencement of the journey, was beautiful in the extreme, and, as the moon, nearly full, appeared through the upper range of arches, had a romantic and beautiful appearance.

Friday, 13th. - Mount Vesuvius was the employment of to-day, and fully rewarded the trouble and fatigue attendant upon seeing it. We were at the foot of the mountain by half-past eleven o'clock. From hence it is usual to proceed to what the peasants call the foot of the summit on asses, but I walked this road. The lower part of the mountain is very highly cultivated, and yields grapes, figs, and other fruit in abundance. This luxuriant vegetation is continued upwards to a considerable height, and takes place upon a soil of lava, partly decomposed and partly pulverised. The road is very disagreeable from the quantity of large loose stones. After crossing an ancient stream of lava, we came at length to the hermitage, or half-way house. The recluse came out to meet us, but though in a black gown, he proved himself not at all deficient in the art of an innkeeper. We stopped there a short time, enjoying the extensive view of both sea and earth presented to us, and then continued our route upwards, until we had reached the foot of the summit. This last road was very rough and hilly, laying over streams of lava, which in many places appeared broken, or thrown together in a very singular manner. At this place the most tiresome part of our journey commenced. What they call the summit - i.e. the mountain formed by the ashes thrown out, and which contains the crater - is constituted by lava and dust. The streams of lava that issue forth at each eruption partly cool on the summit, and remain there, and are afterwards covered by the ashes and stones thrown out. This collection of course has the altitude[199] naturally taken by a heap of small rolling bodies, and added to this great degree of inclination, it has the disadvantage of being a very bad foundation for the feet, continually receding as the foot advances; nevertheless, by the aid of strong sticks and two or three restings, we attained the top by about half-past two o'clock. Here the volume of smoke and flame appeared immense, and the scene was fearfully grand. The ground beneath us was very hot, and smoke and vapour issued out from various spots around us. On the top of the summit rises a small mountain, which from a distance appears covered with sulphur. This we ascended, and then came to a resting-place, from whence the mouth of the volcano, and part of the crater were visible. From here we had a fine view of the fire. The wind was very favourable, and blew the smoke from us, and at times we could see the flames breaking out from a large orifice with extraordinary force, and the smoke and vapour ascending in enormous clouds; and when silence was made the roaring of the flames came fearfully over the ear. We then advanced to a piece of ground thrown up on the edge of the crater, and were then within 100 (feet?) of the orifice from whence the flames issued forth. Here we had a fine view of the crater, appearing as an enormous funnel, and the smoke issuing forth in abundance from most parts of it. It was incrusted in many places with the same yellow substance before observed, and which Sir H. Davy said was muriate of iron[200]. After having stood here a few minutes, we were obliged to retreat with rapidity, for the wind, changing suddenly, brought the smoke upon us, and the sulphurous acid gas threatened suffocation. I incautiously remained to collect some of the substances, and was then obliged to run over the lava, to the great danger of my legs. Having gained our former station, we remained there for a time to observe things in more security.

There appeared to me to be two very distinct species of smoke or vapour - that which proceeded from the mouth of the volcano was very dense, of a yellow-white colour, and rolled away in the form of cumuli. From the odour of that which had been thrown on us by the wind, it appeared to consist principally of sulphurous acid gas and water. From other places a white vapour arose which disappeared rapidly as steam would do, and from the faint odour it possessed appeared to be very little

---

199   Thus in BJ, presumably 'attitude' was intended.
200   iron chloride.

else but steam. Sir H. kindly explained to me that all, or nearly all, the water which was condensed by the mountain, and which would otherwise form streams and springs, was volatilised by the heat, and was one principal cause of the smoke. On the spot where we were a very considerable heat was evident, and in cavities in the lava it was too strong for the hand to bear; and a boy who came up with us cooked some eggs by this heat, and laid them out with bread and wine as a repast. In these cavities a very evident odour of muriatic acid and chlorine was perceptible, and the various substances of white, red, and yellow colours appeared to be muriate of iron.

Where the heat was not too great, the ashes at the top were very moist, from the condensation of water volatilised from below. At one spot where we were, a man poured some wine into a hole, where the heat was so great as to cause a strong ebullition, and the wine immediately evaporated. At some little distance from this spot a white sublimate appeared on the lava in certain spots which proved to be muriate of soda. Having observed everything that was visible at this time, we began, at about three o'clock, to descend, and found the task as disagreeable almost as the ascent, though much more rapid. The asses appeared at an immense distance below us, and the space between them and us was a steep plane of rolling ashes. The descent of this part reminded me very strongly of the descent from the Alps, and the principal difference was, that in the last case we sank and rolled in snow, and in the present in ashes.

Having, however, continued to slide to the bottom, we again got on a less inclined path, and proceeded towards the hermitage. In the descent the streams of lava, which at various times had issued out from the mountain, appeared before us as rivers, and were extremely distinct from the nude soil by their black and barren appearance. The lava appeared exactly as I expected it would do. In many places the liquid or soft portion beneath had been covered by loose masses, which occasioned a rough and rugged surface; and in some parts it had flowed clear and uncovered, and had taken the various curved forms and marks where it had met an obstacle. It was of various colours and densities, graduating from the densest kind to almost pumice.

About the middle of the mountain were various fragments of a green primitive rock, which Sir H. said had been shot out of the mountain. In about two hours we gained the bottom, and proceeded homewards.

Saturday, 14th. - To-day was again devoted to Vesuvius; but the party was much larger, and the hour much later than yesterday, the intention being to see it in the night. We were at the foot of the mountain by half-past four o'clock, and gained the summit by about half-past seven o'clock. During our climb upwards many beautiful views were highly enjoyed, and the evening light on the mountains and promontories was very fine. Some rain fell as we approached the top, which being volatilised by the heat made a much greater appearance of vapour than yesterday; added to which the fire was certainly stronger, and the smoke emitted in far greater quantity. The wind had changed since yesterday, but was still very favourable to our intention, and carried the smoke and vapour in a long black line over the hills to a great distance. It now became dark very quickly, and the flames appeared more and more awful - at one time enclosed in the smoke, and everything hid from our eyes; and then the flames flashing upwards and lighting through the cloud, till by a turn of the wind the orifice was cleared, and the dreadful place appeared uncovered and in all its horrors. The flames then issued forth in whirlwinds, and rose many yards above the mouth of the volcano. The flames were of a light red colour, and at one time, when I had the most favourable view of the mouth, appeared to issue from an orifice about three yards, or rather more, over.

Cloths were now laid on the smoking lava, and bread, chickens, turkey, cheese, wine, water, and eggs roasted on the mountain, brought forth, and a species of dinner taken at this place. Torches were now lighted, and the whole had a singular appearance; and the surrounding lazzaroni[201] assisted not a little in adding to the picturesque effect of the scene. After having eaten and drunk, Old England was toasted, and 'God save the King' and 'Rule, Britannia' sung; and then two very entertaining Russian songs by a gentleman, a native of that country, the music of which was peculiar and very touching.

Preparations were now made for the descent; so taking an earnest view of the crater, we began, at half-past eight, to slide down as before, but with an increase of difficulties, for the uncertain and insufficient light of a waving and fickle torch was not enough to show rightly the path. And the increase of number caused an increase of evils, for, not proceeding in a line, those before ran great danger from the rapid descent of large fragments loosened by those behind; and the cries of alarm were very frequent - and, indeed, some that I saw would have endangered the life of any person against whom they might have struck. Having, however, reached the bottom of the summit, the asses were mounted, and at about eleven o'clock we found ourselves in the village at the foot of the mountain. During our descent, the beautiful appearance of the fire frequently drew the attention of all persons, and the long black cloud, barely visible by the starlight, appeared as a road in the heavens.

Got home by half-past eleven o'clock, highly pleased and satisfied with the excursion.

Friday, June 3rd. - Remained at Terni to-day, employing the time in an excursion to the waterfall of the same name. The cascade is situated at the distance of five miles from the village, and is considered the finest and highest in Europe. It is formed by the lake Velino, which

---

201   The lowest class of Naples, living by odd jobs or begging.

falls into the Nera from a height of above 200 feet. Ascending from the
village, we passed first by the river after its fall, which was much swelled
by the rains, and increased my expectations of the cascade. Its colour
was very white and turbid. After a while we arrived at the summit of
the fall, and saw the stream, of great size, pass with impetuosity to the
edge of the fall. Turning a little on one side, we came to a spot where
the fall was visible: and here truly the scene was beautiful. The view of
the country alone is very fine and from an eminence a fine view of the
valley and the distant mountains is obtained. But the fall is what attracts
the first notice and calls the attention with an immense roaring. The
rocks are perpendicular and the water falls nearly free in a stream of the
purest white. The force with which it descends causes a considerable
quantity to be dispersed in the air in mists and fine rain; and this
produced the beautiful phenomena of the rainbow in the utmost
perfection. Our situation was the most advantageous for this effect, and
the prismatic colours appeared with extreme vividness in an arc of nearly
two-thirds of a circle of about 200 feet in diameter. The red outer and
more faint rainbow was also visible. The water in its descent carried a
vast body of air with it into the recess below, which was forced up again
by the curling stream. This was produced in a very curious and singular
manner. The water thrown up from the bottom of the fall by the
concussion condensed and gathered together in small streams, which ran
down the sides of some low rocks opposite to the fall, and situated in the
stream; but these streams, on passing over the projecting parts of the rock
into the free air, were arrested by the ascending current of air, and were
broken into minute drops, and disappeared. Advancing still further, we
came to a small summer-house, or arbour, at the end of a projecting
rock, which gave us a direct and opposite view of the fall, which here
appeared in full force and grandeur. After admiring the scene for a
while, we walked through a beautiful country to the lake from whence
the stream proceeded. The vegetation here is extremely luxuriant, and
woodbine, geraniums, myrtles, thyme, mint, peppermint, &c scented the
air in the walk. The nature of the old lake was shown in a very
interesting manner. The base of this part is travertine or calcareous
matter deposited by water, which appeared in strata and as stalactites; in
many places agates appeared in the limestone. They had surrounded a
nodule of limestone as a thick shell, and afterwards had been inclosed
by a further deposition of calcareous matter. Chert also occurred. This
cavity was formerly the bottom of a lake which deposited these matters,
but a passage was cut for the waters and by this means a great extent of
country recovered. We came at length to the present lake and taking a
boat rowed on it for some time to enjoy the scenery. The water of the
river is slightly opaque but the lake is beautifully clear. It is surrounded
by mountains of fine form and situation and the views are delicious. In
the distance appeared the mountains which separate the kingdom of
Naples from the Pope's dominions and snow was observed on them in
considerable quantities. On returning to that part of the lake from which

we set out, we observed fishermen dragging. Here many water plants were growing beneath the surface of the water; and I observed many streams of oxygen gas ascend from them, liberated by the rays of a bright sun. We now returned to the fall and again enjoyed our former views; but the rainbow was still more beautiful than before for from the respective situation of the sun the eminence and the fall a bow of three-fourths of a circle was attained. We descended the mountain to gain the bottom of the fall and in going there passed through a grove of orange trees in full blossom and which scented the gale[202] to a distance of many yards. And at a spot nearly opposite to the bottom of the fall, we found that it was not one fall only but three successive falls that conducted the water to the bottom, the first only being visible from the summit. The other falls are not so high as the first and take place amongst enormous rocks and masses, breaking the water into two streams which unite again at the bottom. The scene here was fine but not so beautiful as above.

We now left the fall and went to the side of the river to observe the deposition which is constantly going on here. The masses of travertine were enormous, forming ledges over the present streams and appearing in various singular forms. The different extraneous bodies which fall into the stream are soon incrusted by the water and in some places masses of leaves are found which are thus covered and give their form to stone. Some poles which had been placed in the water to form a ledge were incrusted nearly to the thickness of half an inch. The waters here are very white. Having enjoyed this interesting place for some hours we returned to the village on the hill and from thence to Terni.

On the way home many fireflies appeared emitting their transient light. I caught several and on arriving at the house endeavoured to ascertain whether the luminous appearance depended on the life of the fly. I found one apparently dead and, separating the part which emitted light from the rest of the body, it appeared filled with a white glutinous matter which when extended and exposed to the air shone for about a minute.

I killed a fly suddenly and separated the matter. It was shining at the moment I killed it but when dead it ceased to shine. On separating the part and exposing it to the air, it immediately shone brightly as when attached to the fly and over the whole surface although only the section was exposed to the air. It at length became dim but on compressing it and exposing a fresh part to the air it shone brightly as at first and thus it continued luminous for above forty minutes. At last it became totally extinct and the same effect took place with other flies treated in the same manner. It is probable, from the intermitting and regular appearance of the light when the animal is flying, that it has a dependance on the respiration; and at least it is evident that air is sufficient to cause this

---

202   Thus in BJ.

matter (probably a secretion) to shine. No heat was sensible to the hands or to the under lip (the most delicate part of the body).

Sunday, 5th. - Continued our way through a fine but hilly country, well cultivated and very gay in appearance. We left the Apennines about midday and entered the valleys where the scenery was beautiful from an accompanying river and the surrounding mountains. Towards the evening we came to a mark of the Romans and one worthy of their name. It was the Flaminian Road, which in this place near the mountain of Asdrubal is cut in the side of a solid rock for the length of more than a mile and a half. Here the scenery was sublime to the highest degree and almost terrific - the enormous overhanging cliffs rendering still darker the shades of evening, and a roaring torrent rolling at our feet. At last the way appeared entirely shut up and we seemed as if on the point of entering the Shades as we passed into the rock, but the passage was short and we soon gained again the open air. This astonishing outlet was cut by the Romans through the rock in order to pass a jutting point and gives the last and highest character to this wonderful road. It is in length about twenty-five yards and sufficiently large to admit a carriage without the least danger. The whole road has been repaired by modern hands, made larger, more commodious, and is now the means of the easiest conveyance where conveyance seemed impossible. The rocks are limestone.

On leaving this pass we entered a country the character of which could scarcely be perceived from the advancement of the evening; but entertainment and delight were not wanting, for the fireflies appeared before and about us in innumerable quantities and at a distance they covered the sides of the mountain and near us they passed over the fields, hovered on the edge or crossed the road, often attaching themselves to the harness and emitting their bright and harmless flashes of light in a rapid and beautiful manner.

Lightning of the finest kind also appeared before us on the horizon and the evening was filled by the phenomena of light.

Friday, 17th. - Saw M. Volta who came to Sir H. Davy, an hale elderly man bearing the red ribbon[203] and very free in conversation.

---

203   Alessandro Volta (1745-1827). The red ribbon denoted membership of the Legion of Honour.

Letter to Mother[204]

Geneva: July 1.

I hope, dear Mother, that you are in good health and that nothing occurs to disturb you or render you uncomfortable and that no changes of a disagreeable nature have happened since I left you. I hope too for the health and welfare of all my friends . . . and that at some time I shall be happy with you all again. I think often and often of you and in thoughts often enjoy your company. I contrast the company of my friends with the presence of strangers and I compare the convenience and cleanliness of home to the want and filth of foreign accommodations. Things run irregularly in the great world; and London is now I suppose full of feasting and joy and honoured by the presence of the greatest personages in Europe. I find reason everywhere to feel proud of my country and find everyone ready to praise her and to honour her virtues. My thoughts run hastily, dear Mother, from one thing to another; but you must excuse it at this moment and attribute it to the urgency of circumstances. I long for the moment when I shall salute all my friends personally; but till the moment arrives I must be indebted to the good and kind offices of others and now of you, dear mother. Remember me to . . . tenderly and affectionately; and remind Mr Riebau &c that I still exist; and if Robert will call at the Institution and tell Mrs Greenwell I wish to be remembered to her I should feel the favour.

Adieu, dear Mother. At present my moments are expired but I still remain and ever shall do on this earth your affectionate and dutiful son,

M. FARADAY

Faraday's Journal

Sunday, July 10th. - Geneva. This evening many glowworms appeared and of four which I had put in a tumbler with green leaves two shone very brightly. I separated the luminous part of one in full vigour from the body. It soon faded and in about ten minutes ceased to emit light, but on pressing it with a knife so as to force the matter out of the skin it again became luminous and continued to shine for two hours brightly. One I found on the floor crushed unawares by the foot. I separated the luminous part of this insect and left it on paper. It shone with undiminished lustre the whole evening and appeared not at all to have suffered in its power of emitting light by the mixture and confusion of its parts, so that it appears to depend more upon the chemical nature of the substance than upon the vital powers of the animal, but at the

---

204   Taken from BJ 143-144. No MS survives. BJ noted 'received 18 July'.

same time it appears from the variations in splendour accompanied by motions in the living animal that it may be much influenced or modified by or in some matter submitted to the powers of the worm. This worm is about six or seven-eighths of an inch in length when at its full size. The skin is hard and horny on the back and of a dark-brown or chocolate colour. The belly is of the same colour but of a lighter shade; the head is small and flat. It has six legs at the fore part of the body. Bands traverse the body and make ten divisions, excluding the neck and head, and the divisions on the back and belly are exactly parallel. It is from the four last of those divisions that the light is emitted in the full-grown worm - most brilliantly from the belly but it often pierces through the thick armour of the back. The light is very bright, sufficiently so to render the printing of a book very distinct, and I have often read my watch by it. It is of a delicate greenish tinge. The worm in its whole appearance resembles greatly a large woodlouse. The male is a fly, fully one-third smaller than the worm and emitting no light. The matter which appears to fill the hinder part of the body in the shining season is yellowish-white soft and glutinous. It is insoluble apparently in water or in alcohol. It does not immediately lose its power of shining in them but it is sooner extinct in alcohol than in water. Heat forces out a bright glow and then it becomes extinct; but if not carried too far the addition of moisture after a time revives its power. No motion or mixture seems to destroy its power whilst it remains fresh and moist, but yet a portion thus rubbed sooner lost its light than a portion left untouched. The time of its continuance in a luminous state was very various and perhaps depends upon the state of the worms from which it was taken. The death of the worm seemed to have no immediate effect upon the illumination of the hinder part, and with respect to the length of time that it continued to shine afterwards it seemed indifferent whether it was left on the body or taken off; but when extinct exposure of the interior to air always caused a fresh emanation of light. I found a worm which emitted light from a very small part of the body and very feebly and for a very short time together. The worm was larger than the ordinary species and had more divisions. The power of emitting light in the ordinary worm seemed proportioned to the age of the animal.

Monday, 11th. - The matter of the worms referred to yesterday still shines. It was detached from the animal at 8.24 and still promises to emit light much longer.

Tuesday, 12th. - The matter was luminous this day at 10.41 though faintly and at twelve o'clock no light could be perceived. The matter had become quite dry and semi-transparent but the addition of water produced no particular effect.

Letter to Robert Abbott[205]

Geneva   Saturday   August 6th 1814

Dear Robert

I thank you and most sincerely for the first letter I have received since I left England, and which allayed in a great measure all the anxious desires I felt for my friends at home; I received it this day and from the Post Masters account, suppose that you must have erred in dating it June; indeed my letter by Sir P. Wilson[206] [to] Ben[207] was not wrote till July had commenced: I am left in uncertainty whether that was the first letter received from me by those in England. I had sent several off before: two departed from Paris, one from Genoa, one from Florence, two from Rome, one from Milan; all by private hands, and with Sir Humphry's Letters; and I have lately sent one by the Post from here to your brother Ben. Of the fate of these I am still uncertain, though I entertain hopes that some of them have arrived and that all will ultimately gain their destination: by the rapidity and security with which your kind letter has reached me, I am in hopes of a plentiful supply of information from my friends in England; and must beg of Ben not to delay longer the departure of the three sheets that are ready; I have heard nothing from my mother or brother, and wish you would be at the trouble to desire them to write again, and to direct to me at Geneva, Post restaunt. – I feel grateful from my heart for you[r] information respecting my mother and friends, and hope that at all times when you write you will feel so far interested in my pleasures & satisfaction, as to inform yourself and me of their health & state – I have heard from many quarters of the late rejoicings and feastings in London; the French & Italian papers have been very eager and forward in proclaiming the deeds and doings of England, and my[208] countrymen come into this quarter from London daily, and are glad to give me information. We have heard also of the Prince's unpopularity, and are sorry that at this time England should have any thing in her to disturb her pleasures, or to cause her shame: things are now in such a state that if she but knew how to use her good fortune, as well as she has supported herself in harder times; she will arrive at the possible climax of happiness & prosperity, and still shine as she ever has done in the front of the nations of the world. – It must be gratifying to you Dear Robert to know, how high a character she bears in the eyes of Europe, and to what a degree of estimation and reverence her firmness & her virtues have raised her. I valued my country highly before I left it, but I have been taught by strangers how to value it properly, and its

---

205   From MS in IEE Archives. Also in BJ 146-149.
206   We cannot identify him.
207   Faraday's friend, Benjamin Abbott.
208   The word 'my' is an insertion by Faraday in the original.

worth has been pointed out to me in a foreign land. In foreign nations alone it is that by contrast the virtues of England, her strength, and her wisdom can be perceived, and for those virtues Englishmen are considered every where as a band of brothers, actuated by one heart, and one mind and treading steadily & undeviating in the path of honor, courage, & glory. All nations reverence them; every individual speaks highly of them; the english are respected, received, & caressed every where for the character of their country: may she ever deserve that character: may her virtues still continue to shine in & illuminate the world: may her path never deviate from the point; but still proceeding in a straight line carry her still farther out into the view of the world, where her character meets with its just and honorable reward.

I am happy to find that you are situated as you wish to be and hope that the good prospect will continue: but I am uninformed how Ben stands in the world, though I hope soon to know from himself. I should be glad to hear of the state of the C.P.S.[209] and of the members whom I best know. I wish that it may prosper and be a means of promoting philosophical knowledge, and I feel partly disappointed that you have not joined your force to theirs; for by your professions of unphilosophycality, I suppose that you have not done so. - I have also commissioned Ben in my last to remember me kindly to Mrs Greenwell of the Royal Institution, & Mr Newman of Lisle Street Lincolns Inn fields, and if you or him would also give my respects and remembrances to my old master Mr Riebau, I should be indebted much for the favour; I feel too grateful for the goodness of Mr de la Roche[210] of whom my mother will give you some account; if he should still be in King Street, or in London, I should like to have my name mentioned to him with thanks on my side; but he is perhaps in France, and if I see Paris again I shall search for him.

During the time I have passed from home many sources of information have been opened to me, and many new views have arose of men, manners, & things, both moral & philosophical. The constant presence of Sir Humphry Davy is a mine inexhaustible of knowledge, & improvement; & the various & free conversations of the inhabitants of those countries through which I have passed, have continually afforded entertainment & instruction. On entering France the dissimilarity between the inhabitants and the people of my own country was strong, and impressive; and entered firmly in my mind. I have found the french people in general a communicative, brisk, intelligent, and attentive set of people; but their attentions were to gain money, and for their intelligence they expect to be paid. Politeness is the general character of the people, a character which they well deserve; but the upper classes have carried

---

209   City Philosophical Society.
210   The bookbinder for whom Faraday worked briefly after completing his
       apprenticeship.

it beyond the bounds of reason, and in politeness they lose truth and sincerity: their manners are very insinuating and kind, their address at once easy & free, and their conversation vivid & uninterrupted; but though it dwell for hours on the same subject, you can scarcely make out what the subject is: for it is certainly the most unfixed, most uninteresting, and unapplicable conversation I have met with. The French language in the Mouth of the people has a softness of such delicacy, as is not to be found in other languages; and in which it is I think very superior to the Italian: this last indeed appears to me to have an effeminate character, of which you may in part judge from the morsel you have sent me; but the french language has a great degree of strength, and expression, and is yet delicate and tender. The Italian language is by far the easiest to learn, from the circumstance of every letter being pronounced in the words the same as when single, and also because there is a greater similarity between the words of the Italian & English languages, than between those of the French & English languages: but however I must not pretend to judge as yet of the character of these languages with precision, since I am but little acquainted with them; though at the same time I have endeavoured to avoid the imputation of idleness.

Civilization seems to have taken different paths in the nations of Europe, towards the end of or rather latter part of her progress. At Paris civilization has been employed mostly in the improvements & perfection of luxuries, and oftentimes in the pursuit has neglected the means of adding to domestic and private comfort; and has even at times run counter to it. In ornaments indeed the Parisians excell, and also in their art of applying them; but in the elegance of appearance, utility is often lost, and English articles which have been formed under the direction of a less refined, but more useful judgement, are often eagerly preferred. At Paris every thing yields to appearance, the result of what is called fine taste; the tradesman neglects his business, to gain time to make appearance. The poor gent starves his inside, to make his outside look well; the jeweller fashions his gold into trinkets for show & ornaments; and so far does this love of appearance extend, that many starve in a garret all the week to go well-dressed to the Opera on Sunday evening: I who am an Englishman, & who have been bred up with english habits, of course prefer english civilization to the civilization of France: and think that my common sense has made the best choice; but every days experience teaches me that others do not think so, yet though[211] I have no right to suppose I excell all those who differ from me, I still am allowed the liberty of forming my own opinion. The Civilization of Italy seems to have hastened with backward steps in latter years, and at present is found there only a degenerate idle people, making no efforts to support the glory that their ancestors left them; but allowing it, & their works to

---

211   The words 'yet though' were inserted by Faraday in the original text.

fall into obscurity; cramped[?] by ignorance, and buried in dust, they seem to have been placed on a happy soil, only to shew forth their degeneracy & fallen state, and Rome is at this day not only a memento of decayd majesty, in the ruins of its ancient ornaments & architecture; but also in the degeneracy of the people.

I find dear Sir that my paper is fast filling, and yet I have but little said, and I fear that I shall incur the imputation I have given to french conversation, but though even in danger of that, I would still write to you as my thoughts run; choosing rather to give you my ideas in an unrestrained though careless way, than to force them into a path assigned & chalked out & which would but serve to cramp & distort these already crooked ilformed things. I have purposely omitted giving in this letter any detailed account of my past travels, since I supposed that you would see those of my Mother & your brother; and I intend shortly to send another full sheet to Ben, with a little of Vesuvius &c. in it. I had before taken the advice you so kindly [gave] me of forming a letter, as you will see by the one I have forwarded by Post; and [I] am in hopes of escaping the stigma attached to a short letter by the present sheet. With respect to our future rout I have but a very general knowledge of it, but I expect it will lay in Germany for a short time, for from hence we shall pass (in 5 or 6 weeks) on the North of the Alps to Venice, and from Venice we shall go to Rome, & there spend the winter; so that any letters that are not sent within a month from the date of this, had better be directed to the Post Office at Rome; where I shall hope to find a parcel: but on this subject I shall give you at a future time more correct information. - I apply daily at the Office for news from England, but yours is the first I have received, and I hail it as the forerunner of many more. Remember me sincerely if you please to Mr & Mrs Abbott, to your sister & to Ben, & favour me by letting my Mother my brother & friends know I am well & wish to be named to them. I shall shortly write to Robert but wait for his letter. Adieu dear Robert for the present & believe me truly & sincerely Yours with all wishes

M. Faraday

Letter to Mother[212]

Geneva Friday, August 19

Dear Mother,

It is with the greatest pleasure that I embrace every opportunity that offers the best chance of communicating with you. At this time a

---

212   Taken from BJ 149-152. No MS survives. BJ noted 'received September 12'.

gentleman, a friend of Sir Humphry Davy's, leaves this place, I believe, early to-morrow and expects to be in England in about twelve days; and shortly after the expiration of that time I hope you will be reading over this sheet of paper. I have written many letters[213] to you from various places, as Paris Sestri Genoa Florence Rome &c and also from here, but I have only received one from England, and it only notices the arrival of one of these. Most of these letters, it is true, were sent by private hands and may yet gain you, but some have left Geneva by post and I am much disappointed in not having yet received answers although I attend daily at the office. The letter I received and which came a welcome messenger from a distant beloved country was written by Robert Abbott,[214] nor am I deficient in gratitude for his kindness, not only as it was a proof of his own friendship and remembrance but as it also quieted my anxieties with respect to you, though in a manner so short that it only excited stronger desires for the letter it mentioned as being written by R. (his brother)[215]. I should have written to R. long ago but I wait for his communication. B. has also a long communication and if it is not on the road beg of him to despatch it immediately, if you receive this before September 1 or 2, but otherwise he must direct it to the Poste Restante, Rome.

Here, dear Mother, all goes on well. I am in perfect health and almost contented, except with my ignorance which becomes more visible to me every day though I endeavour as much as possible to remedy it. The knowledge that you have let your house and that it has been doing its office to you almost since the day that I left you was very pleasing, and I hope sincerely that you enjoy health and strength of mind to govern it with your accustomed industry and good order. The general assurance of A. that all friends were in perfect health was much to know but I want a more particular detail, for amongst so many it is almost impossible but that some varieties and changes must occur. I must beg of you to return my thanks to ---; Mr Riebau also might not be displeased to hear the name of his former apprentice.

It is needless, dear Mother, to tell you that I wish you well and happy and prospering - you must know that my wishes cannot be otherwise; and it is the same thing with ---; and yet though it is needless I cannot help but say so. I expect that we shall leave this place, where there is very little indeed except fine weather and a beautiful view of Mont Blanc to detain us, about the middle of September when we shall ascend a little northward and see a little of Germany, passing round the Alps to Venice, and having seen that place for a day or two we shall then take the most convenient road down Italy to Rome. It is Sir Humphry's intention to be at Florence about the middle of October and at Rome about the middle of November, but till we arrive there we shall be

---

213   None appear to survive except those reproduced in this volume.
214   The letter is not extant.
215   Thus in BJ.

constantly moving about and I shall therefore be able to receive no letters after I leave this place until I get there, but there I shall expect to find a whole packet. As letters are about a fortnight on the road between here and London, any letters sent after the first or second of September are likely to reach Geneva after I have left it and will then probably be lost or very much delayed, and consequently you will be so good as to act accordingly. When you write into the country, remember me to all friends there and also to all who may ask after me at home. There are some persons to whom I should be glad to be remembered but as it is possible that such remembrances might raise unjust ideas and observations I will delay them until I return home again. At present, dear Mother, good-bye (for when writing I seem to talk to you and on leaving my paper it appears to me as a farewell). Farewell then, dear Mother, for a short time when I hope again to find myself amongst you.
Yours with the firmest affection,

M. FARADAY

Letter to Benjamin Abbott[216]

Genève Sept 6th 1814

Dear Ben,

It is with extreme pleasure that I pursue a correspondence which I find is not to be impared either by time absence or distance a correspondence which has been dear to me from the first moment of its existence which I have found full of pleasure and which I have never regretted and its continuance continually gives me fresh proofs that it will ever remain as it has been a strong & irreproachable source of instruction and amusement. I thank you dear Ben as earnestly as I can do for your long and kind letter which I shall endeavour to answer as well as I can though not in such a manner as it ought to be. I have not I can truly assure you enough time to write you a letter as long as your own. I have a great deal of occupation which leaves me but little time to myself and my Journal is much behind hand and as we leave this place in eight or nine days I shall have difficulty in arranging my things and clearing up my papers. My head at this moment is full of thoughts respecting you and me respecting your uneasy situation and mine which is not at all times pleasant and what I expected[;] your last letter has partly collected those thoughts and I shall probably state some of them on

---

216   MS letter in IEE Archives. Also in BJ 152-159 and LPW. This letter was received by Benjamin Abbott on 17 September. He wrote to Faraday on 20 November and that letter is published in LPW but is not reproduced here.

this sheet of paper. - I must beg of you also[217] to acknowledge on my part the receipt of your brother's second letter and the receipt of a second one from my brother. I had them both on Augt.31 eight days after the post date they gave me great pleasure and I shall not delay longer than is convenient thanks under my own hand but I will here desire of you Dear Ben to inform my friends that I wish whatever letters they will send me may be directed to me alone or to me at Sir Humphry Davy or chez Monsieur le Chevalier Davy. I have already given this notice in a letter to my brother[218] but for security (for I should wish it to be attended to) I give it again to you well knowing that you will do every thing I can wish. - I feel a pleasure which I cannot describe on perceiving the interest you take in my - i.e. our - friends in Weymouth Street and I hope to return and be grateful for your attentions they are such as I expected from a friend and they deserve better acknowledgements than I can give but I trust words are as little wanting from me to Ben as from Ben to me. In my last letter to my brother I wrote a few lines to Peggy but I unaccountably forgot to thank her for her present which I received with yours and I know of no way of compensating for my slip than by engaging you to thank her for me. I feel great very great interest in Peggy she has talents in a high degree accompanied by a strong and rapid memory and a willing mind and were knowledge to be communicated to her by those who know how to lead a child by attention to their numerous and simple questions and a soft and pleasing demeanour I should hope to see her at one time what I should like to be myself. With the thanks you will give my love and answer fully if you please any questions she may put to you respecting me or the country where I am or may be. I was very happy to hear of Mrs Greenwell's health and hope you will repeat your commission and my remembrances. Sir Humphry was glad to hear that she was well. I hope you will see Mr Newman again and name me to him and if he would remember me to Mr Fincher[219] I should feel much obliged. I remember Mr Fincher on more accounts than one and he will understand me if Mr Newman tells him that I often think on our conversation together and wish I were at home. Some doubts have been expressed to me lately with respect to the continuance of the Royal Institution. Mr Newman can probably give a guess at the issue of it. I have three boxes of books &c there and I should be sorry if they were lost by the turning up of unforeseen circumstances but I hope all will end well (you will not read this out loud) - Remember me to all these if you please - and "now for you and I to ourselves".

I was much hurt in mind to hear of your ill health and still more so to understand your uncomfortable situation for from what I have felt

---

217   Faraday crossed out the word 'also'.
218   This letter does not survive.
219   We cannot identify Mr Fincher.

at times I can judge of your feelings under such a painful bondage. I am as yet but young Ben very unacquainted with the world with men and manners and too concious of my ignorance to set up for a moralizer but yet dear friend I have not passed on to this day without a little experience and though not endowed with the acutest powers of mind I have been forced to notice many things which are of service to me and may be useful to you if they are I shall not repent the trouble I give you and if they are not you must attribute them to the warmth of my feelings for you - You are you inform me in a situation where gain only is the object where every sentiment is opposed to yours where avarice has shut out every manly feeling where liberal thoughts and opinions are unknown where knowledge except as it is subservient to the basest and lowest of feelings is shut out and where your thoughts of not looking to the acquisition of money are censured and where liberality and generosity never enter. These are things which I know to be so opposite to your mind and inclination that I can well conceive your feelings and as if it were to increase those feelings this disagreeable situation follows one that was perfectly pleasant and agreeable. In passing through life my Dear Friend every one must expect to receive lessons both in the School of Prosperity and in that of adversity and taken in a general sense those schools do not only include riches & poverty but every thing that may cause the happiness and pleasure of man and every feeling that may give him pain. I have been in at the door of both those schools nor am I so far on the right hand at present that I do not get hurt by the thorns on my left. With respect to myself I have always perceived (when after a time I saw things more clearly) that those things which at first appeared as misfortunes or evils ultimately were actual benefits and productive of much good in the future progress of things[;] sometimes I compared them to storms and tempests which cause a temporary derangement to produce a permanent good sometimes they appeared to me like roads stony uneven hilly and uncomfortable it is true but the only roads to a good beyond them and sometimes I said they were clouds which intervened between me and the sun of prosperity but which I found were refreshing reserving to me that tone and vigour of mind which prosperity alone would enervate & ultimately destroy.

I have Ben sincerely observed that in the progress of things circumstances have so worked together without my knowing how or in what way that an end has appeared which I could never have fancied and which circumstances ultimately shew could never have been obtained by any plans of mine. I have found also that those circumstances which I have earnestly wished for and which ultimately I have obtained were productive of effects very different to those I had assigned to them and were often times more satisfactory than ever a disappointment would have been. I have experienced too that pleasures are not the same when attained as when sought after and from these things I have concluded that we generally err in our opinions of happiness and misery.

I condole with you Dear Ben most sincerely on the uneasiness of
your situation but at the same time I advise you to remember that it is an
opportunity of improvement that must not be lost in regret & refining.
It is necessary for man to learn how to conduct himself properly in every
situation for the more knowledge he has of this kind the more able is he
to cope with those he is at times sure to meet with. You have under your
eye a copy of thousands and you have the best opportunites of studying
him in noticing his errors you will learn to avoid them what he has good
will by contrast appear more strongly you will see the influence of the
passions one on another and may observe how a good feeling may be
utterly destroyed by the predominance of an opposite one you will
perceive the gradual increase of the predominant sentiment and the mode
in which it surrounds the heart utterly debarring the access of opposite
feelings. - At the same time dear friend you will learn to bear uneasy
situations with more patience you will look to the end which may reward
you for your patience and you will naturally gain a tone of mind which
will enable you to meet with more prosperity both the prosperity &
adversity of your future fortune. Remember that, on leaving your
present situation you may find a worse one and that though a prospect is
fair you know not what it may produce.

You talk of travelling and I own the word is seducing but travelling
does not secure you from uneasy circumstances. I by no means intend to
deter you from it for though I should like to find you at home when I
come home and though I know how much the loss would be felt by our
friends yet I am aware that the fund of knowledge and of entertainment
opened would be almost infinite but I shall set down a few of my own
thoughts feelings &c in the same circumstances. In the first place then
my dear Ben I fancy that when I set my foot in England I shall never
take it out again for I find the prospect so different from what it at first
appeared to be that I am certain if I could have foreseen the things that
have passed I should never have left London. In the second place
enticing as travelling is and I appreciate fully its advantages and pleasures
I have several times been more than half decided to return hastily home,
but second thoughts have still induced me to try what the future may
produce and now I am only retained by the wish of improvement. I have
learned just enough to perceive my ignorance and ashamed of my defects
in every thing I wish to seize the opportunity of remedying them. The
little knowledge I have gained in languages makes me wish to know more
of them and the little I have seen of men & manners is just enough to
make me desirous of seeing more added to which the glorious opportunity
I enjoy of improving in the knowledge of Chemistry and the Sciences
continually determines me to finish this voyage with Sir Humphry Davy,
but if I wish to enjoy those advantages I have to sacrifice much and
though those sacrifices are such as an humble man would not feel yet I
cannot quietly make them. Travelling too I find is almost inconsistent
with religion (I mean modern travelling) and I am yet so old-fashioned
as to remember strongly (I hope perfectly) my youthful education and

upon the whole malgré the advantages of travelling it is not impossible but that you may see me at your door when you expect a letter.

You will perceive Dear Ben that I do not wish you hastily to leave your present situation because I think that a hasty change will only make things worse, you will naturally compare your situation with others you see around you and by this comparison your own will appear more sad whilst the other[s] seem brighter than in truth they are for like the two poles of a battery the ideas of each will become exalted by approaching them - But I leave you dear friend to act in this case as your judgement may direct hoping always for the best I fear that my train of thoughts have been too dull in this letter but I have not yet attained to the power of equalizing them and making them flow in a regular stream if you find them sad remember that it was in thinking on you they fell and then excuse them.

I felt much interested in reading the philosophical part of your letter and congratulate you upon the advances which you must now make and it was doubly pleasing to me as it shewed me that no circumstances could overpower the industry of your active and vigilant mind. I felt highly flattered in understanding the good opinion that was entertained of my friend at the Surry Institution but I was still more pleased at learning his determination since it shews me that he can so easily and successfully combat & overcome pride by humility.

With respect to Boyle's Statical Baroscope I am not sure that I know the instrument. I suppose it is an exhausted flask that is balanced. The experiments are I suppose made with several at a time of different sizes and of different glasses, for as glasses vary in their particular ratio[220] of expansion by heat it will cause variations in the results but I can give no opinion on it - Sir Humphry works often on iodine and has lately been making experiments on the prismatic spectrum at Mr Pictet's[221] these are not yet perfected but from the use of very delicate air thermometers it appears that the rays producing most heat are certainly out of the spectrum and beyond the Red rays. Our time has been employed lately in fishing and shooting and many a Quail has been killed in the plains of Genévè and many a trout and grayling have been pulled out of the Rhone. - Go as usual to Weymouth Street and give my kindest love to them all and if you have not time ask them to do so in the City remember me to Boyer Magrath Castle[222] &c. and kindly to Mr & Mrs Abbott & your Brother & Sister - I need not say dear Ben how perfectly I am yours

Adieu

M. Faraday

---

220   The words 'in their particular ratio' were inserted by Faraday in the original.
221   Marc Auguste Pictet (1752-1825), scientist and founder-editor of the
       Bibliothèque Britannique, later the Bibliothèque Universelle.
222   All members of the City Philosophical Society.

Faraday's Journal

Thursday, Oct. 13th. - Vicenza. We left this place for Padua about half-past ten o'clock. The country flat but the scene interesting from the peculiar time of the year, it being the vintage. In many places they were treading down the grapes and collecting the juice and the roads were filled with men and women carrying large baskets of the fruit. In the market at Vicenza the finest were at four sols of the country, equal to about one penny English, the pound. The Italians seem to know the value of this product of their country and talk of it as a thing essential to their living and the grape is very much respected amongst them. The postilion's whips are universally made of the vine, five or six of the year's branches being twisted together and tied at the top and bottom with packthread - and this makes the handle; and the poor horses are thus honourably and everlastingly flogged by whips of the vine. Begging has increased wonderfully since we left Germany, indeed it is almost the birthright of modern Italy. All are beggars in some way - the innkeepers by the postilion and by the ostlers beg and the poor people of the country universally lay aside their work and run by the carriage begging. A shepherd will leave his flock at half a mile distant to beg at the roadside as the carriage passes and the women will leave their huts and occupation to beg at the door. The children who are more agile and brisk commence by certain ceremonies. Some will, on seeing a carriage at a distance, lie down in the middle of the road and kiss the ground, then rising on their knees they remain in a praying position until it comes up to them, and on its arrival they run to the side and beg in monosyllables of Carità, caro Dio &c &c. Unless sent away with something more to their liking than words, they will follow the carriage for nearly a mile. Others dexterously tumble head over heels five or six times till the carriage approaches and then proceed as the former ones and others vary the ceremonies still further. This detestable habit of universal begging is imbibed by the children even with the mother's milk and if they are not ready and prompt in their supplication they are punished by the parent and enjoined to still further efforts. It must produce a humiliating and depressing effect on the mind of the people in general and appears as a curse spread over the country.

Thursday, Oct. 20th. - Pietra Mala.[223] On arriving this morning we made a halt to see the remarkable phenomenon called in this country Il fuoco della pietra mala or Fuoco di ligno[224] which is about a mile to the south of this little village. The account that I had heard of this phenomenon was as follows - namely that from a certain spot of ground

---

223   Pietramala - the meaning is 'evil rock'.
224   Literally, 'the fire of Pietramala' or 'the fire of wood'.

about ten or twelve feet square situated on the side of the mountain and which appeared to be the same with the neighbouring soil several flames of various sizes broke forth and were constantly burning. Some of these flames were about a foot in diameter and height and others were not more than an inch or two in measure. In some places they were blue, in others red, and in the nights of rainy weather so bright as to illuminate the neighbourhood to a considerable distance. If water was thrown on the flame it would extinguish it for an instant but soon it would spring up with redoubled force – that combustible bodies could be easily burnt by the flame but that the soil there appeared the same as in the neighbourhood and, when not actually covered by the flame, not at all hot or even warm – that M. Bernouille says water will easily extinguish it but that the country people say heavy rains only serve to augment its force and that it was considered as the remains of an ancient volcano.

Also that there were two other places in the neighbourhood of Pietra Mala but in different directions where flames were observed at times but rarely, and that at another place a fountain existed the waters of which were continually boiling and inflamed on putting a light to them. This fountain was called L'Acqua bollente.[225]

Though it was raining hard yet that of course would not deter Sir Humphry from visiting these places but at the same time it made us wish to be as quick as possible. Sir Humphry therefore went to the first place and I went to the Acqua bollente conducted by a man of the village who carried some fire some straw and some water. I found the place in a cultivated field not far from a mountain apparently of limestone. It was simply a puddle perhaps formed by the present showers of rain. Much gas rose from the earth and passed through the water which made it appear boiling and had given rise to its name but the water and the ground were quite cold. I made another puddle with the water we brought near the one I found there and I saw that the gas rose up through it also and it appeared to be continually passing off from a surface of more than eighteen inches in diameter. The soil appeared deep and close to the spot supported vegetation readily. The man inflamed some straw and then laid it on the ground, immediately the gas inflamed and the flame spread to some distance from the straw over the surface of the earth waving about like the flame of weak spirits of wine, this flame burnt some moments. On putting a light to the bubbles which rose through the water they inflamed and sometimes a flame ran quickly from them over the whole surface of the water. I filled a bottle with the gas but I could not distinguish any smell in it. In pouring water into the bottle and lighting the jet of gas that came out a large clear flame was obtained. The whole of this flame was a very pale blue like spirits of

---

225   Literally, 'boiling water'.

wine. It inflamed paper and matches[226] readily as might be expected, and when I held a dry bottle or knife over it they appeared to become dim by condensing water but this was uncertain as the weather was so rainy. The water had no taste and seemed pure rain water. I brought some of it and the gas away and returned to the village.

Sir Humphry Davy told me that it was exactly similar to the one he had been to except in the size of the flame which was at his place nearly four feet in height and diameter. The men extinguished it three or four times and it did not take fire spontaneously. It inflamed immediately on applying a light and burnt with a blue colour similar to spirits of wine. It rose from the earth between some stones but Sir Humphry saw no volcanic remains in the neighbourhood. The gas and the water were preserved for experiments at Florence.

Wednesday, 26th. - To-day a few hours were spent in the examination of the gas from Pietra Mala. The experiments were made at home but the imperfection of the instruments admitted of no accurate examination. It was detonated in a long closed tube with oxygen over mercury by means of phosphorus and it appeared probable that it contained carbon and hydrogen; but no certain results were obtained.

Thursday, 27th. - In the now almost deserted laboratory of the Florentine Academy Sir Humphry to-day made decisive experiments on the gas. The detonating tube was made with platina wires inserted in it to take the spark and various detonations were performed. $2\frac{3}{4}$ths of the gas which appeared to have remained unaltered from the time I had collected it were detonated with $5\frac{1}{4}$ of the oxygen and diminished to 3 and by agitating the remaining gas with a solution of pure potassa it diminished to half a part. It appeared therefore that water and carbonic acid had been formed and Sir Humphry concluded from the proportion that the gas was light hydrocarburet pure. When detonated with $2\frac{1}{2}$ times its volume of chlorine it diminished to about 1 and charcoal was deposited on the sides of the tube.

Saturday, 29th. - We left Florence this morning about seven. Women who ride here - and there are great numbers that do constantly - sit across the horses. We passed three genteelly-dressed ladies to-day who were riding so. They seemed good horsewomen: one of them had a very restless pony to manage.

The love of ornaments in the lowest order of people and their inability to purchase them is an observation one must make in every part of Italy but it struck me particularly to-day perhaps because it was some

---

226   The reference is to a sulphur match (a wood splint coated with sulphur which takes flame readily). Matches in the modern sense of something which can be struck to produce a flame were not invented until 1827.

festa and because I had little else to observe. In many of the poor people that we passed shoes and stockings were wanting, the clothes were in rags and dirty but to make amends large silver hearts were stuck in their breasts and enormous combs and pins of the same metal and another instrument consisting of a bar about six or seven inches long knobbed at each end with balls as large as walnuts and likewise silver was stuck in the hair. Those who had shoes had them literally covered by the buckles and though the leather was left to clean itself yet they take care to show the precious metal. Their pipes too are things in which they delight to show their taste and splendour.

Monday, November 7th. - This morning a man was punished by the civil authority close to our house and the mode deserves notice for its singularity and its cruelty. I observed the first day we came here a gallows fixed up in the Corso next to our palace which was not up when we were here before. It was about thirty or thirty-six feet high, a large pulley was fixed at the end of it and a strong rope ran through the pulley. A stone was fixed in the earth behind the gallows with an iron ring in it. This morning the crowds began early to collect bout the place and I learnt that some one was to suffer and about nine or half-past the man was brought by a guard to the spot. He was placed under the gallows with his hands tied behind him and the rope which belonged to the instrument was fixed to his hands. He was then drawn up to the top and let down again and was thus mounted three times. It generally happens that from the way in which the man's hands and arms are placed - namely behind him - dislocation of the shoulders ensues and the man is crippled for life and this effect is more certainly produced as the crime of the man is greater. In the present case the man was drawn gently up and let as gently down again but sometimes the motion is so rapid and violent as to put the sufferer to the greatest agony and twist his whole body with pain. I saw the man after the punishment was finished. He was carried out of a neighbouring house where some restorative had been given to him. He was surrounded by an armed guard. His hands were tied behind and on his breast was hung a large tablet with Per insolenza al militare on it. I heard that he had thrown mud at some soldiers. He seemed but little hurt by the punishment and walked away with a firm steady quick pace.

Letter to Mother[227]

Rome, November 10, 1814

Dear Mother,

Time goes very strangely with me - sometimes it goes quick and at other times the same period seems to have passed slowly; sometimes it appears but a few days since I wrote to you and the next hour it seems like months and years. This is owing to the nature of the mind of man which looking to what is at a distance when occupied by present circumstances sees it not in its true form and state but tinged by its own cast and situation. But though thus volatile and apparently unstable yet I am at all times, dear Mother, glad when I can by any means make an opportunity of writing to you, for though however short the distance of time since the last letter may be yet I have always something I should like to say and indeed the moment a letter is out of my hands I remember something forgotten. It is now a long time if I may trust to my feelings and the mode of measuring time since I had any communication with you except by thought and indeed longer than I had expected for I was in hopes of finding at the post-office here at least three or four letters for me; but as they are not come I content myself with anticipating the pleasure yet to be enjoyed of perusing them. Since I wrote to you or to England we have moved over a large and very interesting space of ground. On leaving Geneva we entered Switzerland[228] and traversed that mountainous and extraordinary country with health and fine weather and were much diverted with the curious dresses and customs of the country. When I come home (unless M.'s knowledge in geography &c anticipate me) I shall be able to amuse you with a description but at present time (excuse the excuse) will not allow me.

From Switzerland we passed through the States of Baden on the lake of Constance (they are very small) across an arm of the kingdom of Wurtemburg and into Bavaria. In this route we had seen though slightly Lausanne Vevay Berne Zurich Schaffhausen and the falls of the Rhine in Switzerland and Munich and many other towns in Germany. On leaving Munich we proceeded to and across the Tyrol and got to Padua and from Padua to Venice. You will remember very well I have no doubt the picture which hung in the parlour over the fireplace and which represented the Rialto and the Great Canal of this town. The first I have had the pleasure of crossing several times and the second I have partly traversed in a Venetian gondola. I cannot refrain from describing very shortly this city which is certainly unequalled for situation and peculiarity in the world. On approaching it by water - the only mode for it is three or four miles from land - the houses appear actually to rise out of the waves for not a bit of ground is to be seen. The walls of the

227   Text from BJ 165-169. No MS survives. BJ notes 'received January 17'.
228   At the time Geneva was still an independent city state.

houses pass into the waters and there seems no landing-place. We entered the city up a canal and went to the hotel even to the very door in our boat. We saw very few places where it was possible to walk but the number of bridges which passed over the canals showed that there were some means of moving about on foot. On walking out next morning I found an immense quantity of alleys and narrow passages by which communication was made from one part of the town to another and at the Place of St Mark Venice is beautiful. But I find I am going to extend my description too far and therefore to be brief this place before it was built upon was a collection of small flat islands over which the sea would wash in a high storm. When the Venetians built upon them they laid the foundations of the houses upon piles. The number of inhabitants increased, the city was enlarged until they had on all sides built into the water. Instead of streets they formed canals - one called the Grand Canal runs windingly through the town and others smaller intersect it in all parts. All the houses on the edges of these canals have water doors with steps where people can pass into and out of the gondolas and it is by these gondolas that all heavy things are conveyed. The internal part of the town is as I have said before intersected by alleys and passages paved with flagstones. One large place is to be found (of St Mark) but no street and a horse is not to be found in Venice. The people talk Italian generally though they have a pure Venetian tongue. Their government is very peculiar and complicated and curious. After seeing Venice for three days we left it and came towards Italy passing Bologna and Florence.

I am always in health generally contented and often happy but as is usual in every state of life wish for that I have not but most for my return home. I envy you the pleasure you must enjoy in each other's conversation and from which I am excluded but I hope you will ameliorate this deprivation as far as you can by thinking at home of me. I mean quickly to write to --, but in the meantime I should be happy to express through you my feelings to them, they cannot for a moment doubt me but at all times the testimony of remembrance is grateful and pleasing. When you see --, give them my love in the most earnest manner you can though indeed it is scarcely necessary for they and -, and yourself, dear Mother, must be conscious that you constantly have it when anything as a letter &c reminds you and them of me, but paper is now scarce and time advanced and I must quickly leave this letter that it may come to you. But again, dear Mother, I beg of you to let me know quickly how you are and how situated as soon as possible. If right present my humble respects to Mr Dyer and my remembrances to Mr Riebau and other friends, not forgetting --.

Adieu, dear Mother, for a short time. As ever your dutiful affectionate son,

M. Faraday

Faraday's Journal

Saturday, 12th. - It is positively affirmed that the civil punishment above spoken of has given so much offence to the people in general that the Pope has ordered it to be abolished.

[On 20th November 1814 Benjamin Abbott wrote a letter to Faraday which he received at Rome. The MS is in the IEE Archives and is published in LPW 24 and, in part, in BJ 169. We have not reproduced it here.]

Letter to Benjamin Abbott[229]

Rome Saturday Nov. 26th 1814

What have I done or what have I said that I am to hear no more from England day passes after day week after week but passes without bringing me the long wished for letters. Did you but know the pleasure they give me did you but know the importance they are of to me certain I am that compassion would induce you to write. Alone in a foreign country amongst strangers without friends without acquaintances surrounded by those who have no congenial feeling with me whose dispositions are opposite to mine & whose employments offend me where can I look for pleasure but to the remembrances of my friends? At home I have left those who are dear to me from a long acquaintance a congeniality of mind a reciprocal feeling of friendship affection & respect as well as for their honor & their virtues here I find myself in the midst of a crowd of people who delight in deceiving are ignorant faithless frivolous and at second sight would be my friends their want of honor irritates me their servility disgusts me & their impertinence offends me and it is with a painful sensation I think of my friends when I remember I cannot do more. Why then do you delay so long that which is the greatest service you can do me and since I have lost your company let me at least have your thoughts since I can not see you let me see the works of your hand. Through my own imprudence I have lost for a time that source I did possess for I have left at Geneva with books those letters I have received from you my brother and yours & which I ought never to have separated so far from me. It is possible I may never see them again and my fears tell me I may never receive any more and even that the possibility exists of my being for ever separated from England. Alas! how foolish perhaps was I to leave home to leave those whom I loved &

---

229   MS in IEE Archives. Also in BJ 169-172 and LPW. This letter was received on
       24 December 1814, according to Abbott's letter of 25 December 1814, which is
       published in LPW but not reproduced here.

who loved me for a time uncertain in its length but certainly long and
which perhaps may stretch out into eternity and what are the boasted
advantages to be gained knowledge yes knowledge but what knowledge,
knowledge of the world of men of manners of books & of languages
things in themselves valuable above all price but which every day shews
me prostituted to the basest purposes alas how degrading it is to be
learned when it places us on a level with rogues and scoundrels how
disgusting when it serves but to shew us the artifices & deceit of all
around. How can it be compared with the virtue and integrity of those
who taught by nature alone pass through life contented happy their
honour unsullied their minds uncontaminated their thoughts virtuous ever
striving to do good shunning evil and doing to others as they would be
done by. Were[230] I by this long probation to acquire some of this
vaunted knowledge. In what should I be wiser. Knowledge of the world
opens the eyes to the deceit & corruption of mankind of men serves but
to shew the human mind debased by the vilest passions of manners points
out the exterior corruptions which naturally results from the interior of
books the most innocent occasions disgust when it is considered that even
that has been debased by the corruptions of many & of languages serves
but to shew in a still wider view what the knowledge of men & of
manners teaches us. What a result is obtained from knowledge and how
much must the virtuous human mind be humiliated in considering its own
powers when at the same time they give him such a despisible[?] view
of return[?] his fellow creatures. Ah Ben I am not sure that I have acted
wisely in leaving a pure and certain enjoyment for such a pursuit but
enough of it I will turn to more pleasant recollections. I am so confident
in you and the few friends I have in England that I am quite sure it is not
from any change of feeling but from unfavourable circumstances that I
have not yet received any letters from you at Rome. The Post is from
here to England much more difficult & uncertain than at Geneva and is
at least 40 days in going & returning. One may frank from here to Calais
or to Florence only and I am advised to do the last because if the Postage
is paid before hand the letters seldom go. I am sorry for this expense
which will thus fall upon you but I am willing to believe that you do not
repine at the postage of a chance letter from me and I hope for an
opportunity when the debt may be cleared. I would not do it but that if
they are paid the chance is reckoned as 4 to 1. Your health dear Ben is
I hope fixed in a state of vigour but I feel some doubts least the season
which is now winter with you may not incommode you. Mr & Mrs
Abbott are I hope well & Miss Abbott & my friend Robert, and all in
the enjoyment of health my _love_ to all and if you would be so good as to
give the same to my mother brother sister &c. you would add still more
to the obligations I owe you. I wrote to my mother by favour a few
(about 10) days ago and hope the letter will reach home. I shall write

---

230   Faraday wrote 'where'.

immediately to the two B's but I hope also I shall soon read as well as write. I am in excellent health & have been continually. We have passed over much ground since we left Geneva & have seen many things & many places very curious & interesting in themselves and in the information they afforded. On leaving Geneva we immediately entered Switzerland a country very interesting not only from its history it boasted freedom & its situation but also from the peculiarity of its customs manners dresses & the character of the people and all these things we had many oppurtunities of observing in the towns of Lausanne Vevay Berne Zurich Schaffhause Uberlingen & many smaller ones as well as on the roads.   Switzerland claims, and with a good deal of justice the preeminence in beauty of country consisting of mountains it abounds in all those forms of grandeur & majesty which strike the mind with awe and even fear and is washed by many torrents which rushing from the mountains change for a while their azure blue into the whitest foam. The dress of the various Cantons were very interesting & amusing. They differed from each other considerably and form an excellent object for the designer series of costumes which include from thirty to forty varieties each peculiar to its town or canton & very well executed are sold in the Print shops of Berne Zurich &c. The observation of the dress of various countries shews in a very perfect manner the variety & invention of the female mind. The dress of the men differ also in [   ]^{231} countries but when compared with the changes in the habiliment [ ] women it appears stationary. The general form is the same in England France Italy & Germany changed slightly by lesser alterations but the women appear in every form that one can conceive sometimes the head undergoes a thousand changes & sometimes the body and to the passing traveller the change of place is shewn first by the change of the women's dress. The people are generally free good-natured & somewhat more hospitable than the French or Italians but they are great cheats and experience lessened extremely the opinion I had formed of them.   They speak German generally, but it is not the pure language but a corrupted Patois. We saw in Swisserland amongst other things the famous fall of the Rhin at Schaffhause it is the largest waterfall in Europe but it is not very high nevertheless the immense body of water which falls over makes it tremendous & magnificent. On leaving Switzerland we entered Germany by the dominions of Wurtemburg but remained in them only two days. What we saw of the country was flat & monotonous. The weather was here very cold & on the 2nd of Octr. we had a sharp frost. On leaving Wurtemburg we entered Bavaria and stopped for 3 days at Munich a very pretty busy looking place with streets well formed & well peopled. But intending to make no stay untill we got to Rome we soon left it and found ourselves amongst the mountains of the Tyrol. This beautiful country which rivals & perhaps even surpasses in many parts Swisserland furnished us with the sublimest scenery for many days we found the

---

231   Blank in MS here and in the next line where opening the seal has torn the paper.

weather here much more moderate than at Munich. At an elevation of above 6000 feet I found wild strawberries growing. We were at Trente on the 10th of Oct. the day on which the Vintage commences a long walk gave me all the pleasures of this jovial day & I found the vineyards full of the happy labourers. The year was not considered as abundant but to me the quantities of fruit appeared enormous. The roads were soon filled with men & women laden with grapes who carried them to the wine press the first process (which was going on every[where]) was to tread the fruit a vat raised upon a waggon served for this purpose. The fruit was thrown in & two or three men trod it down the juice ran out by a small hole into vessels placed to receive it & was then taken away to be fermented. We passed from Trente by Bassano Vicenza &c. to Padua & then turned off to the left hand to Venice a place I had long wished to see. My curiosity was perfectly satisfyed we stayed there but 2 days, but that was sufficient to see the place in a general manner. You will know the peculiarities of Venice & its situation too well to render it necessary that I should endeavour to describe it.

From Venice we proceeded by Ferrara Bologna Florence Levano Arezzo Foligna Narni &c. to Rome & arrived here on 2nd of November & intend to stop here some time. Between Bologna & Florence at a little distance from the last city we stopped at Pietra Mala to see a phenomenon in natural history called il fuoco di Pietra Mala. At a little distance from the small village of the same name there is a place in the side of a mountain where much gas continually issues out of the earth from between some loose stones and in another place in an opposite direction where a small puddle exists the same phenomena appears when a light is applied to this gas it inflames at the first place a large flame of 4 or 5 feet high & 3 or 4 in diameter arises & in the second it spreads to a little distance over the water. The carriage was stopped at Pietro Malo in the midst of a heavy shower. Sir Humphry went to the first place & I went to the second accompanied by a peasant carrying some straw & fire on arriving at the spot I found the above mentioned puddle apparently formed by the present rains[?] and the gas bubbling up in considerable quantities through it. I could find but a very slight smell somewhat resembling spirits of wine the peasant applied fire to the ground & disturbed the earth a flame immediately spread over the surface to the distance of 4 or 5 inches & burnt for several minutes untill the wind extinguished it on applying light to the surface of the water the gas arising also inflamed & burnt some moments. The flame was very pale & in the day time scarcely perceptible but readily set fire to paper matches &c it was like the flame of spirits of wine. I filled a bottle with the gas it had a very faint smell & on pouring water into a bottlefull of it & holding a light at the mouth a jet of flame was obtained. It did not explode with [ ] its volume of atmospheric air. I brought a bottleful of the gas away & some of the water & at Florence Sir Humphry made experiments on it. (The ground was perfectly cold & also the water). Thursday 27 Octr was occupied at the Academy at Florence with the above gas. 2¾ of the gas were detonated with 5¼ of oxygen and the remainder equalled 3. but on agitating it with a solution of pure potassa it diminished to ½ a volume. From this experiment considered the gas as being light hydro carburet pure. When detonated with 2½ times its volume of chlorine which was done to separate & demonstrate the presence of the charcoal it diminished to 1 & charcoal lined the tube. The water was nothing more than rain water.   The phenomena is extremely singular & I believe unique in its nature. The quantity of gas that issues out from the principal place is enormous and there is no proof that fire has anything to do with the formation of it the country is not at all volcanic & it is doubtfull whether the source of the gas is near at hand or at a great distance. Sir Humphry Davy knows that it may originate from a mine of fossil charcoal but everything is conjecture & it still remains a source of investigation[?].

In my last letters I gave you a rough account of various things that had occured up to Rome & meant to continue it on but as we are now on the same ground & shall go over the same roads again I shall continue the subject on from this letter. My time is extremely occupied so that I can scarcely look in my Italian books & I have been three days in manufacturing this letter. I beg pardon for the inattentions you will find in it & hope that you will [   ]²³² by it in writing to me but will give me some of your usual interesting letters.   I hope that long before you receive this I shall hear from you. I again desire you as a favour & a service to see my friends [ ]. Tell me in your answer how Margaret goes on in her learning. I feel much interested [ ] Institution & should much like to know its probable issue. Remember me to Mr [ ]an & Mrs Greenwell. I hope that if any change should occur in Albemarle Street Mr Newman would not forget my books. I prize them now more than ever. Give my Love again to your family & mine. Adieu dear Friend

M. Faraday

Wednesday 30 Nov.
1814

P.S. Thermometer 60° Fahrenheit!!! not much above the ordinary temperature
Barometer 29.7

---

232   Several words are missing here and in the following few lines where the paper has
        been torn in opening the seal.

Letter to elder sister[233]

Rome, December 21, 1814

Dear Sister,
    . . . When I think of you the first image that forms in my mind is
that of what I left you. Things appear unchanged and the same now they
were a twelve-month ago - Mr G[234] is working before the screen, you
behind it and Sarah is taking her first steps. 'Tis true I can fancy
changes and do fancy them but it is a thousand to one that I fancy them
true and these fancies chase one another about until the whole becomes
confused and rubbed out and the first and last strong and clear
impression remains undisturbed and uninjured not to be removed by the
imagination but by facts.
    Saturday, December 24th. - Hail to the season! May it bring every
blessing down upon you may it fill your hearts with gladness and your
minds with contentment may it come smiling as the morn which ushers
in the glorious light of a summer's day and may it never return to see you
in sorrow and trouble! My heart expands to the idea that Christmas is
come for I know that my friends in the midst of their pleasures will think
of me. Amongst you Friendship will celebrate it - here 'tis Religion.
You will have sincerity amongst you and we hypocrisy. This is a season
in which modern Rome shows forth her spirit her churches (in number
innumerable) are filled with the crowd who in the same hour fill the
streets with licentiousness and riot. For the last week no balls have been
allowed and no theatres or places of amusement were or are yet opened.
To-night the religious rites begin at Santa Maria Maggiore (a beautiful
church) in honour of the Virgin and the child Jesus will be represented
in a beautiful cradle richly decked with jewels and gold. Masses will be
performed at this church all night and to-morrow all the other churches
will be open - St Peter's amongst the rest. After to-morrow the Pope
loses his power for a week or more and the Carnival begins and this
Carnival raises all my expectations for the accounts I have heard of it
make it a scene of confusion and folly. Professed fools (deserving of the
title) parade the streets and hold fearful combats armed with sugar-
plums. Religious clowns and every other kind of character fill the streets
and the whole world goes in masks. The theatres are opened. Puppet-
shows shine in every corner and the Italian character blazes in its full
vigour. Such are the scenes with which I am surrounded but I draw from
them to contemplate those I fancy passing at home in which I hope to
join again and which to me will recur with tenfold pleasure.
    But, dear Sister, though this frivolous spirit occupies the whole
mind of a modern Roman and debases that empire which once stood like

---

233   Elizabeth. Text taken from BJ 172-174. No MS survives.
234   Adam Gray, Elizabeth's husband.

a Colossus over the whole world yet still this city the seat of that empire draws forth involuntary awe and respect. How often have I wished that Mr D[235] could see what I saw that he could wander with me over the mighty wilderness of ruins the Colosseum presents - sometimes mounting sometimes descending walking in the steps of the ancient Romans and leaning against the walls which resounded with their voices. Again the ancient baths each rich as palaces and large as towns here their paintings are to be seen in their original station the marble which they had worked and the walls which they had formed. Again the columns of Titus and Antoninus or rather of Marcus Aurelius enormous in size covered with beautiful sculptures and formed of marble.

Again a thousand other objects as tombs temples statues pyramids pillars road &c which continually fill the eye of a stranger. D would be delighted with them and his art and skill would enable him to bring faithful ideas of them home . . .

God bless the little one and you all together. I shall never feel quite happy til I get amongst you again. I have a thousand things to say but I do not know which to say first and if I followed my mind I should never get to an end . . .

Adieu, dear Sister, for a time and believe me to be ever and unalterably your loving and I hope beloved brother

M. Faraday

[Benjamin Abbott wrote to Faraday on 25 December 1814. That letter is published in LPW 25, but is not reproduced here.]

Letter to younger sister[236]

Rome: December 29, 1814

Dear Margaret,

I am very happy to hear that you got my letter and I am as happy to say that I have received yours. I had the last yesterday and to-day I write you an answer. I am greatly obliged to you for the information you give me and for the kind interest you take in my health and welfare. Give my love with a kiss to mother the first thing you do on reading the letter and tell her how much I think on her and you. I received a letter from Mr. A. late, who told me in it that you had spent a day in his house

---

235   We cannot identify Mr D.
236   Text taken from BJ 175-177. No MS survives.

and he thought that you were very well pleased with it, and when you to to Mr. B.'s again you must return humble thanks for me and say how much I am honoured by his remembrance. I hope that all your friends are well and I suppose that your correspondence is now very important. I am glad to hear that my niece E. is in favour with you but you quite forgot to give me any news of S. I suppose thoughts of the first had put the last out of your head, which head I fancy has gained with these little relations a great deal of importance.

I am also pleased to hear that you go to school and I hope that you have enough to do there. Your writing is not improved quite so much in one year as I expected it would be when I left home but however it is pretty well. Your I's are most in fault. You must make them thus, *I I I I* with smaller heads. My questions about Rome and Naples I did not expect you could answer but I wished you to look into some book at school or at Mr Riebau's or elsewhere and give me the answers from them at the same time fixing them in your memory. I gave them to you as lessons and I still hope you will learn them. I hope that you do not neglect your ciphering and figures, they are almost as necessary as writing and ought to be learned even in preference to French. Of this last you say nothing but I suppose you still work at it. I will tell you my way of learning the words. When in my grammar or in other books I meet with a word (and that happens often enough) that I do not know, I first write it down on a fair sheet of paper, and then look in my dictionary for its meaning, and having found it I put it down also but on another part of the same sheet. This I do with every word I do not know very well and my sheet of paper becomes a list of them mixed and mingled together in the greatest confusion - English with French and one word with another. This is generally a morning's work. In the evening I take my list of words and my dictionary and beginning at the top I go regularly down to the bottom. On reading the words I endeavour to learn their pronunciation and if I cannot remember the meaning in the other language I look in the dictionary and having found it endeavour to fix it in my memory and then go to the next word. I thus go over the list repeatedly and on coming to a word which I have by previous readings learned I draw a line over it, and thus my list grows little every evening and increases in the morning and I continually learn new and the most useful words from it. If you learn French and pursue this plan at home you will improve in it very quickly. I must now dear M. put an end to my letter. I have written to R. lately and shall write to him again soon tell him. I wish him every happiness. Give my warmest love with your own to mother (and say I wrote about a month ago by favour to her) and to R. and B. and Mr. G. and the little ones and all your friends. Write again at an opportunity to your affectionate brother,

M. FARADAY

Wednesday, 11th. - I have done nothing to-day but search for books which I cannot find - an employment which though not successful yet pleased me as it took me into booksellers' shops.

Letter to Robert Abbott[237]

Rome Jany 12th 1815.

Dear Friend,

I hasten to make use of another opportunity which the kindness of Sir Humphry Davy offers to me to pay you a letter which I have long but unwillingly owed you but the number I have written to England lately by favour & by post made me fearful of being called an intruder and I at once was afraid to add and afraid to delay adding to those I had written - but the pleasure I find in writing letters has determined me to run the risk of gaining the title which I am almost confident I shall never receive from you. In writing to a friend I actually talk to him and I see no reason why I should not talk as often as possible and if neither you nor I complain of the <u>sterling value</u> of our questions & answers I do not see why others should and therefore I shall make no scruple of writing letters to you and also to Ben whenever the fit takes me and though they may perhaps not allways come as cheap as this yet I trust you will never burn the paper before reading it though the fate may be good enough for them afterwards.

I acknowledge with thanks the receipt of your last kind letter at Geneva[238] but as I left it there in a large parcel of books & papers I cannot write you a formal answer. Soon after arriving at Rome I wrote four or five letters to my Mother my brother & Ben and after receiving one from my Brother Robert & one from Benjamin[239] I wrote to my Sister & to your brother in acknowledgement and three days ago I sent one off by post to my old Master's Mr Riebau. In these several of which I suppose you have received I have given short sketches of our last journey from Geneva through Swisserland a part of Germany across the Tyrol and along Italy to this Place, this City of Rome, and as I suppose you have heard those accounts it would be tiresome to you to repeat them here. I shall therefore give mere observations upon present circumstances - Rome is far more amusing pleasant & interesting now than it was the last time we were here. We have now swarms of English about us who

---

237   MS in IEE archives. Not previously published.
238   Benjamin Abbott's letter of 25-26 December 1814, published in LPW but not reproduced in this volume.
239   Presumably Benjamin Abbott's letter of 25 and 26 December 1814, published in LPW but not reprinted here.

keep this part of the world constantly in motion. The season is more interesting the weather is very mild & fine & the Carnival approaches added to which time has added a little more to my stock of Italian & I find myself more capable of searching out & enquiring for things & information. Christmas would have passed very dull here had it not been for the foreigners that is the English and a few French & Germans that are here, as it was it was chearful and we kept Christmas day, Christmas week & Twelfth day with a Ball, feastings & other games suited to the season & the place. The inhabitants kept it in an hypocritical religious way and you would have smiled to see the midnight ceremonies at Santa Marie Maggiore.

It happened about 3 weeks ago that a Senator was elected & upon the addition of a member to that august body the Senate of Rome it was said that fine doings would take place, a procession was promissed to please the mob & give them a high opinion of their new director but as the weather happened to be bad on the day fixed it was very unceremoniously put off as a thing of little importance, now this opinion of it may be very correct[?] for I should think 't was of no importance at all, but for such an arrangement to be altered which had been made by the government tended to give very light ideas of the government itself. The procession however took place on the first day of the year when the weather was beautiful & the town shown forth in great splendour. In the morning preparations were made by spreading mould along those streets through which the procession was to pass in its way from Monte Cavallo the Popes Palace to the Campidoglio or Capitol where the Senate house stands about 12 o clk. The fronts of the houses in those streets were highly decorated by tapestry & hangings suspended from the windows many pieces of which had moved from the floors & many from the beds; about 3 o'clk the procession moved & made a pretty sight enough but certainly not what I expected for a Roman Senator. It was clean & in good order but short & neither the Pope or the Cardinals were there.

I went a few days ago to see the Gallery & part of the Museum at the Capitol and was very well entertained by them. They showed me there an ancient bronze figure of a wolf sucking Romulus & Remus. It is said that when Caesar was assassinated this was struck by lightning and two places in the hind legs are shown where the bronze has by some means been melted or destroyed. There were many other things in the Museum extremely interesting as antique statues[?] bronze casts & some stupendous fragments of Collossi, but these things must be described by amateurs and judges more accurate than me.

It is now ½ past 12 o'clk at night and both the hour & the paper tell me to make an end. I do not as yet know who will bring this letter to you but I hope it will go safe. If I have time I shall put it with one to my Brother but I am not certain of that. I have not forgot your Commission & the first opportunity that occurs I shall send it home to you. In return I must beg you to give my warmest love to My Mother Brother Sisters, to Mr & Mrs Abbott to your Sister & to Benjamin & my remembrances to Boyer, Magrath, Castle &c. I shall soon write Ben an answer to his letter & tell him what I have seen of water falls. Adieu Dear Friend till I read your next letter.

Yours Ever & sincerely

M. Faraday

Faraday's Journal

Tuesday, 24th. - The Carnival has been the constant subject of conversation for several weeks not only of strangers but of the Romans themselves. Willing to give importance to their city and its diversions they tell us what it had been and what we might expect to see, and from what they said and from their evident anxiety for its arrival and their preparations for it I confess I expected a great deal. 'Tis a season in which the poorest beggar will enjoy himself even though he strip his hole of everything it contains and when the whole population of a city like Rome joins together for the same end one may be allowed to expect that the end will be well attained and especially when it is pleasure.

To-day is the first day of the Carnival which is commenced by the long-talked-of races. I felt very anxious to see these races for the singularity of the place added to my having heard of them in England raised expectation very high. But as is generally the case with high expectations mine were disappointed. About four o'clock I walked to the Corso and found it very promising. It was lined on both sides with an immense number of people some sitting on the scaffolds and some standing about. Guards were placed on each side at the edge of the foot pavement (or that which represented it) and the middle of the street was occupied by carriages and people that were passing up and down it (being the common Corso of Italy). Seeing that there was yet plenty of time I walked up to the Piazza del Popolo where the Corso begins and from whence the horses were to start. There I paid my five baiocchi and took my seat on a scaffold fixed under the obelisk and which commanded a view of the whole length of the Corso, and I amused myself for a short time in observing the preparations which were certainly worthy of a much better thing . . . The Corso had been lengthened by two rows of booths into the middle of the place and was terminated by the scaffold on which I stood. Just before the scaffold several strong posts were fixed up on each side of the ground and a very thick rope stretched across at breast high. The booths at each side were filled with persons of consequence and the whole place was covered with carriages the owners of which wished to peep but could not unless they chose to herd with the multitude. At a quarter past four two pint pots were fired off and on a repetition of the signal in about five minutes the carriages all turned out of the Corso by the nearest side streets and the pedestrians only remained in it. The guards now took their stations in a more orderly way, a troop of horse rode gaily to the end of the Corso but soon returned to the commencement at full speed and then no person was allowed to be in the open space between the guards.

The horses five in number were now brought out by the master and his men who were gaudily draped on this occasion and the horses themselves were not undecorated though to them as it often proves to us their finery afterwards proved a pain.

A very slight harness made of cord &c was put on them to which were attached four tin plates one on each flank and one on each shoulder. Over these were fixed four balls of lead set with six or eight sharp spikes each, they hung by a string or chain five or six inches long. Their heads were decorated with a plume of feathers of various colours.

There was not much time to be spared when the horses came out, as soon as they saw the Corso and the people they were eager to set off. Six or eight men held each horse by his shoulders his tail his mane &c. But with one horse these were not sufficient. He got over the starting rope and dragged the men with him and the master cried out he could hold the horse no longer. The trumpet sounded the rope dropped and the animals were instantly at full speed. They took the middle of the Corso and proceeded very directly to the other end. The plates of tin soon flew off and the spiked balls beating the sides of the animals and the cries of the people as they passed were enough to frighten any English horse. They started very regularly but one was soon six or eight yards before the others and got in first. The mode of stopping them is by a cloth stretched across the end of the Corso at sight of which they generally stop of themselves but lest they should run against it and bring it down a second is fixed up a few yards behind the first.

They profess to make the Corso open for any person's horse but they are generally the property of one man and trained up to the sport. it is said that some few years ago an English horse ran with the others but not knowing the customs of the country he passed the barriers and ran out of Rome. In the time of the French government the prize was 300 francs for the first horse but the thing which repays the master is the subscription of the people in general. He parades the street for two or three days before the races with his horses mounted by riders carrying flags &c and he gets abundantly sufficient to remunerate him and to leave a pretty surplus besides.

Letter to Benjamin Abbott[240]

Rome Jany 25th 1815

Dear Benjamin

I begin this letter in a very cheerful state of mind which enables me to see things with as correct an eye as it is possible for my weak judgement to do unless indeed I see them too favourably but at all events I hope that you will not have occasion in your answer to this letter to repeat what you have said in your last. I have received both the letters you have directed to me at Rome[241]. I have too much to say at present to waste words in thanking you for them you know how great their value is to me and the return I can give that will be most wellcome to you is to answer them. It happens fortunately indeed that the first is in part answered and I am not sure I can say much more in return for it on this sheet of paper or even on another if I happen to extend my blotting[242]. It was my intention when I read it to give you some account of the various waterfalls I had seen but now I have more important & fresher subjects to treat of & shall reserve them for another time by important I do not mean important in itself but only with respect to the waterfalls and you must understand the word in that sense. I cannot however refrain from saying how much I feel obliged to you for your information respecting the health &c. of my mother & our family and hope that you will always have the charity to continue such information as far as lies in your power.

Though it may appear somewhat consequential that I begin the letter with my own affairs, yet such is my intention at present. You found me in the last squabbling almost with all the world and crying out against things which truly in themselves are excellent and which indeed form the only distinction between men and beasts. I scarce know now what I said in that letter (for I have not time to take copies of them as you supposed) but I know I wrote it in a ruffled state of mind which by the bye resulted from a mere trifle. Your thoughts on knowledge which you gave me in return are certainly much more correct than mine that is to say more correct than those I sent you which indeed are not such as I before and since have adopted but I did not mean to give them to you as any settled opinion they ran from my pen as they were formed at that moment when the little passions of anger and resentment had hooded my eyes.

You tell me I am not happy and you wish to share in my difficulties. - I have nothing important to tell you or you should have

---

240   MS in IEE archives. Also in BJ 180-187 and LPW.
241   These do not survive.
242   This letter occupies two sheets of paper.

known it long ago but since your friendship make you feel for me I will trouble you with my trifling affairs. - The various passions and prejudices of mankind influence in a greater or less degree every judgement that men make and cause them to swerve more or less from that fine line of rectitude and truth into the wide plains of error. Errors thus generated exert their influence in producing still greater deviations untill at last in many points truth is overthrown by falsehood and delusive opinions hold the places of just maxims and the dictates of nature. Nothing shews this truth more plainly than the erroneous estimation men make of the things the circumstances and the situations of this world. Happiness is supposed to exist in that which cannot possibly give it. Pleasures are sought for where they are not to be found. Perfection is looked for in the place from which it is the most distant and things truly valuable are thrown aside because their owner cannot estimate them. Many repine at a situation others at a name and a vast multitude because they have neither the one nor the other.

I fancy I have cause to grumble and yet I can scarcely tell why. If I approve of the system of etiquette and valuation formed by the world I can make a thousand complaints but perhaps if I acted influenced by the pure & unsullied dictates of common sense I should have nothing to complain of and therefore all I can do is to give you the circumstances.

When Sir Humphry Davy first made proposals to me to accompany him in this voyage he told me that I should be occupied in assisting him in his experiments in taking care of the apparatus and of his papers & books and in writing and other things of this kind and I, conceiving that such employment with the opportunities that travelling would present would tend greatly to instruct me in what I desired to know & in things useful in life, consented to go. Had this arrangement held our party would have consisted of Sir Humphry & Lady Davy the Lady's maid la Fontain Sir H's valet & myself - but a few days before we came off la Fontaine diverted from his intentions by the tears of his wife refused to go & thus a new arrangement was necessary. When Sir H.- informed me of this circumstance he expressed his sorrow at it and said he had not time to find another to suit him (for la Fontaine was from Flanders and spoke a little Italian as well as French) but that if I would put up with a few things on the road untill he got to Paris doing those things which could not be trusted to strangers or waiters and which la Fontaine would have done he would there get a servant which should leave me at liberty to fill my proper station & that alone. I felt unwilling to proceed on this plan but considering the advantages I should lose & the short time I should be thus embarrassed I agreed. At Paris he could find no servant to suit him for he wished for one that spoke English French & a little German (I speaking no French at that time) and as all the English there (ourselves excepted) were prisonners and none of the French servants talked English our want remained unsupplied but to ease me he took a

Lacquasse de Place[243] and living in a Hotel, I had few things to do out of my agreement. It will be useless to relate our progress in the Voyage as it relates to this affair more particularly a thousand reasons which I have now forgot caused the permanent addition of a servant to our family to be deferred from time to time and we are at present the same number as at first. Sir Humphry has at all times endeavoured to keep me from the performance of those things which did not form a part of my duty and which might be disagreeable and whenever we have been fixed I have had one or more servants placed under me we have at present although in an hotel two men servants but as it is always necessary to hold a degree of subordination in a house or family and as a confidential servant is also necessary to the master and again as I am the person in whom Sir Humphry trusts it obliges me to take a more active share in this part of my present occupation than I wish to do & in having to see after the expences of the family I have to see also after the servants the table and the accomodations.

I should have but little to complain of were I travelling with Sir Humphry alone or were Lady Davy like him but her temper makes it often times go wrong with me with herself & with Sir H. She is haughty & proud to an excessive degree and delights in making her inferiors feel her power she wishes to roll in the full tide of pleasures such as she is capable of enjoying but when she can with impunity that is when her equals do not notice it & Sir H is ignorant of it she will exert herself very considerably to deprive her family of enjoyments. - When I first left England unused as I was to high life & to politeness unversed as I was in the art of expressing sentiments I did not feel I was little suited to come within the observation and under the power in some degree of one whose whole life consists of forms etiquette & manners I believe at that time that she hated me and her evil disposition made her endeavour to thwart me in all my views & to debase me in my occupations. This at first was a source of great uneasiness to me and often times made me very dull & discontented and if I could have come home again at that time you would have seen me before I had left England six months as I became more acquainted with the manners of the world and those things necessary in my station and understood better her true character I learned to despise her taunts & resist her power and this kind of determined conduct added to a little polishing which the friction of the world had naturally produced in your friend made her restrain her spleen from its full course to a more moderate degree. At present I laugh at her whims which now seldom extend to me but at times a greater degree of ill humour than ordinary involves me in a fray which on occasions creates a coolness between us all for two or three days for on these occasions Sir H- can scarcely keep neuter and from different reasons he can scarcely choose his side.

---

243   Laquais de Place - a locally hired servant.

Finally Sir H.- has no valet except myself but having been in an humbler station and not being corrupted by high life he has very little occasion for a servant of that kind & 'tis the name more than the thing which hurts - I enjoy my original employment in its full extent and find few pleasures greater than doing so.- Thus Dear Ben I have answered your kind inquiries by a relation of my circumstances things which were not of consequence enough to put in a letter before you asked for them. - As things stand now I may perhaps finish the voyage in my present company though with my present information I should not hesitate to leave them in any part of the world for I now know I could get home as well without them as with them. At all event when I return home I fancy I shall return to my old profession of Bookseller for Books still continue to please me more than any thing else.

I shall now my dear friend turn the subject or rather change it for Philosopy and hope in so doing to give you pleasure in this letter. I say this more confidently because I intend to give you an account of a paper just finished by Sir Humphry of which one copy has already been sent by Post as a letter to the Royal Society and all the experiments & demonstrations of which I have witnessed.

When we were at Naples the Queen gave Sir H- a pot of colour which was dug up in their presence it contained a blue paint in powder. At Milan a gentleman had some conversation with Sir H- & gave him some pieces of blue glass from Adrian's Villa at Rome and since we have been here this time the opportunity afforded & the former hints have induced Sir H.- to undertake an examination of the ancient Grecian & Roman colours with an intent to identify them & to imitate such as were known. I shall give you a very brief account of this paper putting down results discoveries & such points as I think will be most interesting to you.

The introduction speaks of the art of painting as it existed in Greece and as it flourish[ed] truly greek in the midst of Rome. Many arguments and authorities are brought forwards to show that even in Italy during the (early part at least of the) Roman ages the art was grecian and was cultivat[ed] by & flourish[ed] under the care of natives of its own country. He concludes the introduction by announcing his chemical labours on this subject.

The second part speaks of the red colours of the Ancients these and indeed almost all the colours came from the ruins of the Baths & Palace of Titus which stand at a little distance from the Coliseum and are wonderfully interesting, from their extent their perfection and their richness[;] of three red[s] found in a pot in these baths two were ochres and the third proved to be red lead these colours Sir H.- recognising again on the walls in various parts of the ornaments. In the chamber & the niche where the Laocoon is said to have been found another red prevaile[d] which proved to be Vermilion. - A classical account is then given of those colours but the history of vermilion is the most interesting amongst[244] the reds. It was prepared by washing the ores of quicksilver & from its beauty & scarcity held a very high price. It used to be placed amongst the precious ointments at feasts & the body of the victor at the Olympic games was coloured with it.

The third part treats of yellows a large pot in the ruins of the baths of Titus contained a yellow colour which was an ochre. The author notices two other yellows which were spoken of by Vitruvius & Pliny[245] auripigmentum & Sandarach[246]. The first he considers as massicot[247] or the yellow oxide of lead and the second as an oxide of lead obtained by a different degree of heat or calcination. Orpiment[248] has not been found amongst the ancient colours.

Fourthly blue colours. Sir H.- found several shades of blue in the baths of Titus on the walls and on pieces of stucco but he found them to be the same colours mixed with different quantities of chalk or whiting when separate from the carbonate of lime a fine blue powder rough to the touch unalterable in its colour by heat but when urged agglutinating together. By analysis it gave Silica Alumina lime potash and oxide of copper and some pieces of blue frit found in the chambers gave the same colour when powdered & the same products by analysis[;] it appears therefore that this colour is a deeply tinged frit powdered & is probably the same as that the ancients called cerulian.

Some blues mention[ed] by Pliny appear to be preparations of lapis lazuli & of the arseniates & carbonates of copper.

The Greeks appeared to be acquainted with a species of indigo.

Blues on some fragments of fresco from ruins near the monument of Caius Castius others in a celebrated antique picture now at Rome and that alluded to as found at Pompeia appear all to be produced from this blue frit.

Pieces of blue transparent glass which have apparently been used for mosaic work and which are very frequent in the ruins are coloured with cobalt & it appears that all the transparent blue glasses are tinged with the same metal and it must be supposed that the knowledge of this metal or at least of its ores has been unjustly denied them by the moderns.

The greens come next in order and these appear to be produced principally by copper & to be the carbonates of that metal. In the vase however a portion of the green earth of Verana[249] was found - Sir H.-

---

244　Faraday appears to have altered 'of' to 'amongst'.
245　Vitruvius Pollio was a Roman architect and military engineer under Augustus, best known for his treatise **De Architectura**. Pliny the Elder, 23-79 A.D., is remembered for his wide-ranging **Naturalis Historia**, which included the use of minerals in the arts, and for his death in the eruption of Mount Vesuvius.
246　Sandarac, also known as realgar or red orpiment, is native arsenic disulphide, used as a pigment.
247　Yellow lead monoxide, used as a pigment.
248　Arsenic trisulphide, a bright yellow pigment.
249　Verona?

considers the substance called chrysocolla as a green colour a combination of copper. He points out the error of those who suppose borax to be chrysocolla and shews that there is no reason for supposing that the Borate of Soda was known to the ancients.

The ancients had beautiful green glasses which were tinged with copper but they did not use them in the state of powder as colours.

The fine Tyrian purple of the ancients comes next under consideration but here more of uncertainty prevails. The circumstances of its being prepared from animal matter prohibits any hope to find it in its original state after a period of 1700 years but not discouraged by the difficulties the author has given some very interesting observations & conjectures on this point. From the description given of this colour by the ancient authors Sir H- was induced to try many experiments on a pale rose-coloured powder found in a vase at the baths of Titus. This colour was destroyed by heat by acids & alkalies. It appeared to be composed of siliceous aluminous & calcareous earth with a little oxide of iron. When mixed[?] with the hyper oxymuriate of potassa & heated a slight scintillation was perceptible and the gas given of precipitated lime water & from these & various other experiments it was evident that the colouring matter was of animal or vegetable origin but which Sir H. was not able to determine though the probability is in favour of the first and of its being the Tyrian purple of the ancients.

Other purples were mixtures of red ochre & the blues of copper.

The blacks & browns of the ancients were easily made out such specimens of black as were found in the baths on pieces of stucco were carbonaceous matter. Pliny speaks of the ink of the cuttle fish of ivory black & of some fossile blacks. The first Sir H- observes is a compound or rather mixture of carbonaceous matter with gelatine - the second was discovered by Apelles - the third was probably ores of iron & manganese - and the author considers the ancients as being acquainted with the ores of this last metal.

The browns are all mixtures of red & yellow ochres with black.

The whites which have been found in the ruins at Rome are all either carbonate of lime (chalk) or a fine aluminous clay - The ancients were acquainted with ceruse but Sir H- has not met with it.

The paper then gives some observations on the mode in which the ancients applied these colours. Their stucco is described which was formed of powdered marble cemented by lime[;] three coats of the stucco were laid on & the powder of each diminished in size from the first to the third[;] when dry & polished it was ready to receive the colours.

The encaustic process is referred to and Sir H- endeavoured to discover if any such a process had been performed upon the walls of the chambers in the baths or in the Aldobrandine picture but could gain no evidence in the affirmative.

In some general observations with which Sir H- concludes the paper he gives a process for making the Azure or Alexandrian frit 15 parts of carbonate of soda 20 parts of powdered flints & 3 parts of copper filings strongly heated for 2 hours will produce the frit which when powdered gives the same fine deep sky blue.

Those colours which are the most permanent are pointed out. Frits are placed first and after frits saturated combination of metals. Animal and vegetable colours are the least permanent.

The colours which the refinements in Chemistry have given to modern artists and which excell the ancient colours in tint & durability are noticed and the cause of their superiority is pointed out & in the last lines some ideas are given on the materials which are best calculated to receive the picture and on the modes of preserving. Canvas impregnated with asphaltum or bitumen is considered as being superior to wood copper or any other substance than is used for this purpose.

I am ashamed Dear Ben to send you this imperfect account of so valuable a paper but I trust that my willingness to give you news will plead my excuse. I hope you will soon read a copy of the paper at large and have no doubt you will perceive in every page the enquiring spirit of the author. - I have long inquired after a sure opportunity of sending a little parcel home and if it were in my power I should pack up a few of these colours for you with your brother's snuff box some books of mine & other little things but as yet my search has been useless however at Naples I may meet with better luck.

I have within the last few weeks altered the plan of my journal and for that purpose have made free with your name but I hope you will allow me to continue the liberty I have already taken. I found myself so much more at ease in writing to you than in writing in my book that latterly I have written in it as if I were talking to you and from this it arises that your name now and then occurs and though not in bad yet perhaps in foolish company and for this I attend your pardon.

I have heard nothing at all of the earthquakes and eruptions you spoke of but expect to be more in the country of them soon - and then for a little of Vesuvius if I have time.

I must not forget the proof you have given me of your feelings truly of friendship in the dilemma and I am extremely sorry that I should in any way have occasioned you embarrassment. I am indebted much to you for your care in concealing such things as you supposed I intended for you alone. They were written for you alone, but at the same time I did not wish that my mother should remain ignorant of them. I have no secrets from her and it was the insignificance alone that made me quiet[?] on the subject. I would rather my mother should see or hear the first sheet of this paper than otherwise for where the causes are open the conduct can be better judged of with this part you may do as you please but there is as yet little in it can interest her and I do not know that I shall add much more.

I must however tell you that we are in the midst of the Carnival a scene of great mirth & jollity amongst the Romans. Last Tuesday 24th it began by the horse race which takes place in the Corso in the middle of the city. Having in London heard of these races I felt much inclined to see them and paid my five baiocci -/3^d for a seat. Before the race commences the people that fill the corso open to the right & left & leave an open space about 18 feet wide. The horses were brought out and placed before a rope at the top of the Corso & on sounding a trumpet the roap falls & the animals start. They go without riders they have a slight harness on just sufficiently strong to hold some leaden balls at the end of a chain. These balls are set with short sharp spikes one is being on each shoulder & one on each flank and as they run the play of the balls pricks them on to their utmost speed. On Thursday & Saturday these races were repeated & today also and on Thursday the masquerade began. This takes place also in the Corso & continues from about 3 till 6 o'clk. Today it was very good & all Rome glittered with Princes Princesses Dukes Lords Spaniards Italians Turks Fools[?] &c. all of which were in profusion. I went this morning to a masquerade ball between 2 and 5 o clk and found it excellent.

Now for news!!! We shall part in a few weeks (pray write quickly) for Naples and from thence proceed immediately to Sicily. Afterwards our road is doubtful but this much I know that application is made for passports to travel in the Turkish Empire & to reside at Constantinople that it is Sir H-'s intention to be amongst the Greek Islands in March and at Athens early in the spring. - Thus you see Ben a great extension is made to our voyage an extension which though it promises much novelty & pleasure yet I fear will sadly interrupt our correspondence. Have the goodness therefore to write quickly & tell all my friends that you can to do the same or I shall not get the letters - I shall make a point of writing to you as long & as late as I can.

I will not pretend to know whether it is time to leave off or not but I think it is impossible for you to get through this letter of 12 pages in less than three or four readings. How it has got to such a length I know not for I have as yet read no part of it over and even now I find I could write you a long letter were this and the subject of it anihilated but I must cut it short. Pray remember me with strongest affection to my mother & friends & to your family (excuse the repetition) and at your opportunities repeat your commission of remembrance to Mrs Greenwell Mr Newman and others - Castle Rupert Magrath &c. I am in a great passion with your brother for not writing to me and must beg of Miss Abbott to scold him well having more time than you.

Adieu dear Friend with you I have no ceremony the warmest wishes that friendship can dictate are formed for you by

M. Faraday

P.S. Do you know any thing of a young lad of the name of George Bramwell. Mrs Meek my Companion has a cousin in London of that name who is in a country house on the river side with a Mr Abbott. She heard me mention the name & supposed that her cousin might be with your Father. Should that be the case she wishes to be remembered to him

and to know how he is in a letter from himself if convenient. Le Donne
Italiani sono sfacciato pigrissimo e sporchissimo come dunque volete fare
una comparazione fra loro e l'Inglese

                                        Adio Caro Amico[250]

Faraday's Journal

Sunday, 29th. - A mask ball takes place to-night or more correctly
it is to begin at one o'clock to-morrow morning and end at six o'clock.

Monday, 30th. - Went in a domino to the mask ball this morning
and was much amused though there were but few people and the greater
number were in their common day-dress. The theatre in which it was
held was a very fine one large and in excellent condition and extremely
well lighted. A vast number of chandeliers were suspended from all parts
of the roof and filled with wax-candles and every box was also lighted
up. The stage and the pit were thrown together by a flight of steps. The
pit was given for waltzing and the stage for cotillon and country dances
and two good bands of music were employed in the theatre. Other rooms
in the wings were thrown open some for dancing and some for
refreshments. The three lower tiers of boxes were shut but the rest were
open to the maskers and the people in the house. A guard of soldiers was
placed in the house to preserve order and a gentleman in black with a
cocked hat sat in the centre box and overlooked the whole. He appeared
to enjoy the scene very slightly and was I suppose there as fulfilling a
duty in looking over the whims of the place.

In the afternoon there was much masking in the Corso and the
sugar-plums which were only seen in the sellers' baskets on the first
evening were now flying in the air. These confetti as they are called are
merely plaster or old mortar broken into small pieces and dropped in a
mixture of whiting but the men take care to sell them dear though the
price generally depends upon the eagerness of the purchaser at any
moment to have them. With these the battles are carried on between
mask and mask or between carriage and carriage. None but masks are
allowed to throw though this rule is transgressed from every window.
The most dreadful contests are carried on between the carriages as they
pass each other and I found the English were much more eager at this
sport than the Romans. I know an English window from which eight
crowns' worth of confetti were thrown this afternoon.

In my way to the Academy Lincei I made a great blunder - I
mistook a burial for part of the masquerade!!! But from the habit of the
priests and mourners who attended it it might be thought the mistake was

---

250   There are several doubtful readings in the Italian, but the meaning is 'Italian women
       are impudent, lazy and very dirty, if you compare them with English women.'

theirs who put religion in those things rather than mine who took it for masking. Their sackcloth coats, very similar to what the masked clowns and punchinellos wear, their enormous knotted cords tied round their waists, their sandals and their caps like a brewer's straining-bag with two little holes for the eyes were as complete a mask as it is possible to make and it was not till by chance I saw the body that I thought it was a serious affair.

Wednesday, February 1st. - Experiments at home all day on a new solid compound of iodine and oxygen which Sir Humphry discovered on Monday. It is formed by the action of euchlorine on iodine which produces at the same time the compound of iodine and chlorine and of iodine and oxygen. Its properties are many and curious and it has enabled Sir H. to demonstrate (abroad) the truth of his ideas respecting iodine and its various compounds and combinations.

Monday, 6th. - Went to this morning's masked ball in a domino and found it very full, as no one knew me at least for some hours I amused myself a good deal with such as I was acquainted with. I stopped there till daylight and then came home.

Tuesday, 7th. - To-day is the last of the Carnival and all Rome swarmed with masks they were in every corner just as you find the fleas there and the quantity of <u>confetti</u> thrown away was astonishing. A race of nine horses cleared the Corso for a short time but as if really to give a long adieu to the season the carriages and masks entered again. They were however restrained from paying the last ceremonies to their departing pleasures for the Pope would not allow of what had always taken place till this year. It had been the custom of the masks to promenade on this the last day with lighted tapers in their hands crying out <u>Mort' è Carnivale</u> but now that the Pope himself was at Rome he would not allow of such a mockery of their burial service which they wish to have considered as something serious.

To-night's ball was the last of the profane pleasures the season allowed them and indeed it was well enjoyed. I found all Rome there and all the English besides. It was too full for dancing and the amusement was principally the jokes of those that were not known to those whom they knew. I was in a nightgown and nightcap and had a lady with me whom I had not seen till that night but who knew all my acquaintances and between us we puzzled them mightily and we both came away well entertained.

Saturday, 11th. - Experiments at home on the new compound of oxygen and chlorine which Sir Humphry discovered a few days ago. It is a gas of a very bright greenish colour which detonates into chlorine and oxygen by a heat a little above that of boiling water. It was detonated in a comparative experiment against chlorine. One volume increased to nearly $1\frac{1}{2}$ in both experiments; but the products of the decomposed new gas contained 1 of oxygen and $\frac{1}{2}$ of chlorine and the products of the detonated euchlorine were 1 of chlorine and $\frac{1}{2}$ of oxygen. A small piece of phosphorus introduced into it caused a spontaneous detonation. A solution of it by its action on solution of the alkalies gradually formed hyperoxymuriates &c.

Letter to Mother[251]

Rome: February 13, 1815

My dear Mother,
   . . . I wrote lately to B. and put the letter in the post I do not know when he will get it or whether he will get it at all but if he does he will tell you that we are going to Greece and Turkey immediately. I thought we were going there but at present things seem a little more unsettled. We go shortly to Naples and if we can from Naples to Sicily, afterwards I know not what road we shall take perhaps we shall go immediately by water to the Archipelago or Grecian Islands or perhaps we may return up Italy again across the Alps see Germany and then pass by Carynthia Illyria and Dalmatia into Turkey. Things being in this state I can say nothing more particular about the road at present though I can tell you to a moral certainty that we are to see Constantinople.
   The mention of these places calls England to my mind now farther from me than any of them and much as I wish to see these places yet the idea of England fills my mind and leaves no room for thoughts of other nations, 'tis still the name which closes the list and 'twill ever be the place I am desirous of seeing last and longest. Our travels are amusing and instructive and give great pleasure but they would be dull and melancholy indeed if the hope of returning to England did not accompany us in them. But however dear Mother circumstances may divide us for a time and however immense the distance may be between us whatever our respective states may be yet never shall I refrain from using my utmost exertions to remind you of me. At that distance to which we may go I shall despair of hearing from you but if it is possible my letters shall find you out and I trust you will never be tired of them . . .
   Give my kindest love to [ ] and [ ] and my remembrances to all who ask you of me. And believe me dear Mother every your most sincere and affectionate son,

M. FARADAY

---

251   Text from BJ 192-193. No MS survives.

Letter to Huxtable[252]

Rome, February 13, 1815

Dear Huxtable,
. . . As for me like a poor unmanned unguided skiff I pass over the world as the various and ever-changing winds may blow me, for a few weeks I am here for a few months there and sometimes I am I know not where and at other times I know as little where I shall be. The change of place has however thrown me into many curious places and on many interesting things and I have not failed to notice as far as laid in my power such things as struck me for their importance or singularity. You will suppose that Sir H. Davy has made his route as scientific as possible and you must know that he has not been idle in experimental chemistry and still further his example did great things in urging the Parisian chemists to exertion. Since Sir H. has left England he has made a great addition to chemistry in his researches on the nature of iodine. He first showed that it was a simple body. He combined it with chlorine and hydrogen and latterly with oxygen and thus has added three acids of a new species to the science. He combined it with the metals and found a class of salts analogous to the hyperoxymuriates. He still further combined these substances and investigated their curious and singular properties.
        The combination of iodine with oxygen is a late discovery and the paper has not yet perhaps reached the Royal Society. This substance has many singular properties. It combines both with acids and alkalies forming with acids crystalline acid bodies and with the alkaline metals oxyiodes analogous to the hyperoxymuriates. It is decomposed by a heat about that of boiling oil into oxygen and iodine and leaves no residuum. It confirms all Sir H.'s former opinions and statements and shows the inaccuracy of the labours of the French chemists on the same subjects.
        Sir Humphry also sent a long paper lately to the Royal Society on the ancient Greek and Roman colours which will be worth your reading when it is printed but if you please for present satisfaction Mr B. Abbott can and will I have no doubt with pleasure read you a short account of it.
        Sir H. is now working on the old subject of chlorine and as is the practice with him goes on discovering. Here however I am not at liberty to say much but you may know that he has combined chlorine and oxygen in proportions differing from those of euchlorine. The new substance is a very beautiful yellow-green-coloured gas much deeper than euchlorine. It explodes when heated with a sharp report and 1 volume gives 1 of oxygen and $\frac{1}{2}$ chlorine nearly whereas 1 of euchlorine gives 1 of chlorine and $\frac{1}{2}$ of oxygen so that the new gas contains four

---

252   Text from BJ 193-195. No MS survives. T. Huxtable was a friend of Faraday's.

times as much oxygen to the same volume of chlorine that euchlorine does.

I beg to be excused for thus intruding subjects which perhaps now have no charm for you for your time I suppose is filled with medicine but I hope you will attribute it to my wish to give a little value at least to my letter and in whatever way you may receive it I will still maintain that Sir H.'s discoveries are valuable. But I find my time runs short though my subjects are not yet exhausted . . .

I present with the certainty of their being accepted the best wishes of yours ever sincerely

M. FARADAY

Letter to Benjamin Abbott[253]

Rome Feby 23 1815

Dear Ben,

Another opportunity draws another letter from me and I believe if one were to occur every day I should be unwilling to let it pass. It is but a week ago that I sent three letters to England by favour and now I am writing again; tis true those were not for you but a month has scarcely elapsed since I put a letter of above 12 pages into the post directed to my friend <u>B.A.</u> This however I am afraid you have not got but I hope it will soon reach you and though its length & its tediousness may perhaps deter you from reading all of it yet I shall be at ease as having fulfilled your request. In it I gave answers to your question respecting my situation. It was a subject not worth talking about but I considered your enquiries as so many proofs of your kindness & the interest you take in my welfare and I thought the most agreeable thanks I could make you would be to answer them. The same letter contained also a short account of a paper written by Sir Humphry Davy on ancient colours (but by this time I hope you have read a copy of the original and I shall therefore say no more about it) and some other miscellaneous matters.

I am quite ashamed of dwelling so often on my own affairs but as I know you wish it I shall briefly inform you of my situation. I do not mean to employ much of this sheet of paper on the subject but refer you to the before mentioned long letter for clear information[254]. It happened a few days before we left England that Sir H-'s Valet declined going with him & in the short space of time allowed by circumstances another could not be got. Sir H- told me he was very sorry but that if I would do such things as were absolutely necessary for him untill he got to Paris he

---

253   MS in IEE archives. Also in BJ 195-198.
254   See above, letter to Benjamin Abbott, 25 January 1815.

should there get another. I murmured but agreed. At Paris he could not get one. No Englishmen were there & no Frenchman fit for the place could talk english to me. At Lyons he could not get one at Montpellier he could not get one, nor at Genoa nor at Florence nor at Rome nor in all Italy & I believe at last he did not wish to get one and we are just the same now as we were when we left England. This of course throws things into my duty which it was not my agreement & it is not my wish to perform but which are if I remain with Sir H- unavoidable. These it is true are very few for having been accustomed in early years to do for himself he continues to do so at present & he leaves very little for a Valet to perform and as he knows that it is not pleasing to me & that I do not consider myself as obliged to do it he is always as careful as possible to keep those things from me which he knows would be disagreeable. But Lady Davy is of another humour she likes to shew her authority and at first I found her extremely earnest in mortifying me. This occasioned quarrels between us at each of which I gained ground & she lost it for the frequency made me care nothing about them & weakened her authority & after each she behaved in a milder manner. Sir H- has also taken care to get servants of the country yclepd[255] Laquaise de place to do every thing she can want & now I am somewhat comfortable indeed at this moment I am perfectly at liberty for Sir H- has gone to Naples to search for a house or lodging to which we may follow him & I have nothing to do but see Rome, write my journal & learn Italian.

But I will leave such an unfruitful subject and tell you what I know of our intended rout, for the last few weeks it has been very undecided and at this moment there is no knowing which way we shall turn. Sir H-intended to see Greece & Turkey this summer and arrangements were half made for the voyage but he has just learned that a quarantine must be performed on the road there & to this he has an utter aversion and that alone will perhaps break up the journey. At Naples he will enquire more particularly about it. Lady Davy wishes very earnestly to go and if Sir H- finds accomodation at Naples and we follow him there I think that we shall still go the voyage if not then we shall turn up Italy & see what Germany contains & perhaps pass over land to the Great Turk. As soon as I hear anything certain I shall let you know and when it is possible for you to write to me I shall not be slack in telling you of it. - There was a captain here & I believe he is somewhere here yet that had a ship off the shores of Rome intended for the use of Mr Hope[256] who is here he goes very soon for England & has a letter from me for your brother one for my mother & one for Huxtable & I hope they will be received. I suppose I have lost many letters from my friends by this unlucky Post affair no letter from England having arrived[?] here during

---

255   named.
256   Not identified.

the last 6 weeks. I expected one from my brother but have been disappointed but I hope the road will soon be opened again.

Since the long letter I sent to you Sir H- has written two short papers for the Royal Society & two or three copies of each have been sent home. The first was on a new solid compound of Iodine & oxygene and proves the truth of his former reasonings. It is made by passing euchlorine into a receiver containing iodine. The second is on a new gaseous compound of Chlorine & oxygen which contains 4 times as much oxygene as euchlorine. It is made by barely moistening hyperoxymuriate of potassa with hydrosulphuric acid and distilling the almost dry mixture by the heat of boiling water a gas comes over which is of a very bright greenish yellow colour, much brighter than chlorine and may be received over mercury on which it does not act[;] water dissolves it rapidly & forms a deeply coloured solution which acts on solution of the alkalis & forms hyperoxymuriates. The gas detonates by a heat a little above that of boiling water and one volume expands into $1\frac{1}{2}$ volumes of which a volume is oxygene & half a volume [is chlorine][257].

The discovery[?] of these bodies contradict many parts of Gay Lussac's paper on Iodine which has [been] much vaunted in these parts. The French Chemists were not aware of the importance [of] the subject untill it was shewn to them and now they are in haste to reap all the honours attached to it but their haste opposes their aim. They reason theoretically without demonstrating experimentally and errors are the results.

I intended at first to give you some account of <u>water falls</u> in this sheet but I fancy only the name will be seen for (not I but) Mr Wells the kind bearer of this letter has no more time to allow me. I trust you will employ a few hours of your time when you can let my mother know I have written to you & if you will consent to shew her the letter at least what is not philosophical I shall esteem it as a favour. Give my [?] love to all my friends both in the East & the West and if you can in the City

I am my Dear Friend

Yours Ever & Faithfully

M. Faraday

Faraday's Journal, March 1815

Friday, March 3rd. - Left Fondi[258] the first two stages rode a saddle-horse. Now though I am no rider yet the circumstance must not

---

257   The paper has been torn here and in the next few lines by the seal.
258   **BJ**, who sometimes confused Faraday's T and F, had Tondi.

be attributed to me alone that the horse and I were twice heels over head but rather it is a wonder that it did not happen oftener in nine miles. A tailor would have said that the horse was religious and that it only did as other Italians do when they grow old and feeble but that did not satisfy me and I would rather have had a beast that would have gone on orderly upon his legs.

Tuesday, March 7th. - I heard for news that Bonaparte was again at liberty. Being no politician I did not trouble myself much about it though I suppose it will have a strong influence on the affairs of Europe.

Thursday, 16th. - I intended this morning to dedicate this day to Pompeii but on Sir Humphry's asking me whether I would go with him to Monte Somma I changed my mind. We left Naples about 10.30 and took the usual road to Resina. The weather was clear the atmosphere heavy, the wind fair for ascending Vesuvius which rose before us as the gates of another world and was still marked by yesterday's fall of snow. At Resina we bought bread and oranges and then began the ascent. After an hour spent amongst the vineyards we came upon the plain of lava and crossed on towards Monte Somma. Here the guide pointed out some particular stream of this matter. We crossed the lava of 1814. Its surface was very rough and craggy as if it had issued out in a state of imperfect fusion and almost ready to become solid at the moment yet it was not more than eleven or twelve inches thick. The old lava (17..?) had a very different appearance. It had been if not more fusible more fluid and had flowed flatter and smoother. It was even thinner than the former.

We now began to ascend the hill of the Hermitage and here the guide pointed out cinders or ashes of the same kind and of the same shower that overwhelmed Pompeii and it is of these and of volcanic products more ancient which Sir Humphry gave to a period of time long before Pliny that this hill is formed. We made no stop at the Hermitage except to view the plain which we had just left below us and to note the directions of the currents. Here the guide again reverted to the old lava of 17..? and related in what manner it was approaching to Naples itself and the rapid advances it made every hour insomuch that it had soon passed many other streams of lava and begun to menace the city when good St Januarius went to it and standing before it with a crucifix in his hand he raised it in front of the burning river and bade it stop which it immediately did and became firmly fixed in the same place. It is not always however that the image or saint possesses such virtue or faith and then curious contests arise between the people and their ineffectual protector and even the Virgin Mary has been so much abused as to have phlegm thrown in her face.

After a little further progress I left Sir Humphry for he intended to see Monte Somma only and I wished to ascend the cone of Vesuvius. I therefore continued my way alone along the lake of lava and soon gained the foot of the cone where I found several asses and eight men who belonged to a company then up the mountain. On hearing that the state of things was altered above and was no longer as when I saw it before I took a guide with me and began to climb. After a little while I saw the company above me just coming over the edge of the hill and it was at this moment I gained a correct idea of the size of this ash hill. From the uniformity of its figure and inclination the eye is deceived and thinks it much smaller than it really is but when I saw some moving spots at the summit and by the guide's assistance distinguished them to be men I was aware in some measure of the immense space between them and me. We continued to ascend regularly except at intervals when we turned round to enjoy the fine view from this elevated spot. The company now approached us sending down a shower of stones before them. The ascending and descending path is different so that no one is in danger from a blow except such as are first of the descending corps but in them inattention would be dangerous. In thirty minutes we gained the edge of the crater and got on flatter i.e. less inclined ground for as to smoothness it was much rougher than the hill. The fatigue of the ascent in a hot sunshine had made me very thirsty. With pleasure I ate with my hand some of the still unmelted snow on the mountain.

This uneven surface presents many spots where the vapours and smoke issue out sometimes even from the centre of rocks of lava, they rise dense and heavy and appear to be sulphurous and carbonic acids with water in a state of vapour. Their effects upon the lava were to bleach it making it of a fine white or yellow colour and in many spots they deposit muriate of iron and muriate of ammonia. The ground is very wet in many places from the melting of the snow and the condensation of the vapours that rose from the interior and the guide from that circumstance promised me a fine view of the crater. After about ten minutes further progress we came to an elevated mass of lava and from thence saw the crater about sixty yards in advance but here we stopped awhile to see it at this distance. The scene was grand in the extreme and cannot be conceived but from the seeing of it. The cloud of smoke rose very rapid and high in the atmosphere and moved off in a side direction so as to leave us without fear of being annoyed by it. The colouring of the place was very strange though brilliant. The smoke at moments took various tinges from the sun on the part opposed to its rays and the opposite side of columns possessed all the sombre black and waving red hues of that which might be supposed to issue from the abyss. The dark burnt ground was irregularly arrayed in many colours of the greatest beauty but they struck the eye as being unnatural. The yellows were muriate of iron and lava with various tints from its natural black colour to white according to the time or the power with which the sulphurous vapours had acted on it. The reds and greens were mixtures of the bleached lava with iron. No sulphur was present in a concrete form and no smell of sulphur except from the vapours of the volcano. The general smell of the place was like chlorine.

From the spot that we now occupied I heard the roar of the fire and at moments felt the agitation and shakings of the mountain but the guide not satisfied with this went forward and we descended some rocks of lava and proceeded onwards towards the very edge of the crater leaping from one point to another being careful not to slip not only to avoid the general inconveniences of a fall but the being burnt also for at the bottom of a cavity the heat was in general very great. I had nearly however been down for whilst stepping skipping &c the guide suddenly cried out to look and I did so though falling. I saw a large shower of redhot stones in the air and felt the strong workings of the mountain but my care was now to get to the crater and that was soon done. Here the scene surpassed everything. Before me was the crater like a deep gulf appearing bottomless from the smoke that rose from below. On the right hand this smoke ascended in enormous wreaths rolling above us into all forms, on the left hand the crater was clear except where the fire burst out from the side with violence its product rising and increasing the volume of volatile matter already raised in the air. The ground was in continual motion and the explosions were continual but at times more powerful shocks and noises occurred then might be seen rising high in the air numbers of redhot stones and pieces of lava which at times came so near as to threaten us with a blow. The appearance of the lava was at once sufficient to staisfy one of its pasty form. It rose in the air in lumps of various size from ½ lb to 25 lbs or more. The form was irregular but generally long like splashes of thick mud, a piece would oftentimes split into two or more pieces in the air. They were redhot and when they fell down continued glowing for five ten or fifteen minutes. They generally fell within the crater though sometimes a piece would go far beyond its edge. It appeared as if splashed up by the agitation of a lake of lava beneath but the smoke hid all below from sight. The smoke generally rose in a regular manner and though the noises explosions and trembling varied much yet the cloud seemed to rise with the same strength and impetuosity. I was there however during one explosion of very great force when the ground shook as with a strong earthquake and the shower of lava and of stones ascended to a very great height and at this moment the smoke increased much in quantity. The guide now said this place was not safe from its exposed situation to the melted lava and to the smoke and because it oftentimes happens that a portion of the edge of the crater is shaken down into the gulf below. We therefore retreated a little and then sat down listened and looked.

After a while we returned. This was rapid work but required care from the heat of the lava and the chance of a fall of some yards. The descent of the cone is made over the softest part that which is most equally spread with ashes and in the finest form. Every step is worth twenty of the ascending ones and it took us four minutes and a half to return over a space which occupied in ascending thirty-five minutes of our time. At the Hermitage I found some acquaintance but not Sir

Humphry and I therefore continued to descend and got to Resina in good time.
I was very glad of this opportunity of ascending Vesuvius for I had heard so many and such different accounts from persons who have lately been up it that I thought it must be in a very changeable state or at least that it had changed much since I saw it last. This it certainly has done and by to-day's walk I have gained a much clearer idea of a volcano than I before possessed.

Monday, March 21st. - We left Naples this morning at five o'clock. The weather pleasant but cool. We pressed forward the whole of the day and fully employed it in getting to Terracina. In passing Fondi we were saluted by the Neapolitan troops who were coming into the town from their recreation by the gate we wanted to go out at. Their salutations were stares hurras hisses groans laughing and chattering and all apparently for want of something to do. There were a great number of them here and the town was more than full with them but for what purpose they are here is as yet unknown.

Wednesday, 23rd. - Rome. The Romans are now in much agitation respecting the motions of Murat[259] and made eager inquiries about his advance &c but they made no preparations to oppose him. The Pope goes to-day from this place and the cardinals will all be off in two or three days more. No post-horses to be had.

Thursday, 24th. - We wanted to go to-day but finding that everybody else wanted to go too and that no horses were to be had we were obliged to delay a little our departure. Everything however was packed up and every means used to set us and our luggage in motion. At last carriage-horses were hired at an immense expense to take us to Cività Castellana to-morrow.

Wednesday, March 30th. - Mantua is singularly twisted by fortifications and outworks and labourers are now employed by hundreds to twist it still more by the same kind of arrangements. Indeed everything is prepared and everybody is preparing for war. Mantua has on this side a very pretty and picturesque appearance but this I fancy it owes in a great measure to the magnificent background given to it by the Alps. We wished to get through the town as soon as possible, but were destined to remain in it some hours. We found some trouble in getting into it and we found still more in getting out of it. The passport was asked for at the outer gate, it was taken into the bureau examined and registered. It was then at the distance of twelve or fourteen yards asked for at the inner gate examined and registered as before and then sent by

---

259   Joachim Murat, King of Naples.

a soldier to the police office. In the meantime we were permitted to proceed to the post-house and there remained. After a while the soldier came back and said Sir Humphry must go to the police-office to answer some questions. In about forty minutes Sir Humphry came back with the permission but it was not good. It had been signed by the police only and not by the commandant. It was to go back again and I went with it. At the police-office I found them examining the passport and I witnessed the several tedious operations of examination registering signing and sealing. The passport then passed the ordeal of their hands and then we got it re-signed or counter-signed by the commandant. All was now valid and we got the horses and considered ourselves in a state of motion but we found it to be intermitting only and not continual. At the gate of exit we were stopped, the passport examined registered &c and the same done at another bureau about twelve yards in advance. During these examinations the traces of a wagon laden with hay broke just as it got on the drawbridge and we had to wait until they pleased to mend them. At last we saw the outside of the town having much against our will remained two hours and a half in it.

Stuttgard, Friday, April 8th. - General Flahault[260] un Français who came here to our hotel was stopped examined and sent back to the frontier with a guard of gendarmes. He came from Paris and wished to go to Marie Louise at Vienna but was much to his disliking disappointed. The people laughed much at him.

Letter to Mother[261]

Bruxelles, April 16, 1815

My very dear Mother,

It is with no small pleasure I write to you my last letter from a foreign country and I hope it will be with as much pleasure you will hear I am within three days of England. Nay more, before you read this letter I hope to tread on British ground but I will not make too sure lest I should be disappointed, and the sudden change and apparently termination of our travels is sufficient to remind me that it may change again. But however that is not at all probable and I trust will not happen.

I am not acquainted with the reason of our sudden return, it is however sufficient for me that it has taken place. We left Naples very hastily perhaps because of the motion of the Neapolitan troops and

---

260 Comte Auguste Charles Joseph de Flahaut de la Billarderie (1785-1870) was carrying official despatches from Napoleon to the Empress.
261 Text from BJ 206-208. No MS survives.

perhaps for private reasons. We came rapidly to Rome we as rapidly left it. We ran up Italy we crossed the Tyrol we stepped over Germany we entered Holland and we are now at Brussels and talk of leaving it to-morrow for Ostend; at Ostend we embark and at Deal we land on a spot of earth which I will never leave again[262]. You may be sure we shall not creep from Deal to London and I am sure I shall not creep to 18 Weymouth Street and then - but it is of no use. I have a thousand times endeavoured to fancy a meeting with you and my relations and friends and I am sure I have as often failed; the reality must be a pleasure not to be imagined nor to be described. It is uncertain what day we shall get to London and it is also uncertain where we shall put up at. I shall be thankful if you will make no inquiries after me anywhere and especially in Portland Place or of Mr Brande. I do not wish to give occasion for any kind of comments whatever on me and mine. You may be sure that my first moments will be in your company. If you have opportunities tell some of my dearest friends but do not tell everybody - that is do not trouble yourself to do it. I am of no consequence except to a few and there are but a few that of consequence to me and there are some whom I should like to be the first to tell myself - Mr Riebau for one. However let A. know if you can.

I come home almost like the prodigal for I shall want everything . . .

I cannot find in my heart to say much here to B. and R. because I want to say it myself and I feel that I am too glad to write it. My thoughts wander from one to another, my pen runs on by fits and starts and I should put all in confusion. I do not know what to say and yet cannot put an end to my letter. I would fain be talking to you but I must cease.

Adieu till I see you, dearest Mother, and believe me ever your affectionate and dutiful son,

M. FARADAY

Tis the shortest and (to me) the sweetest letter I ever wrote you.

[The party returned to London on 23 April 1815.]

---

262   Faraday subsequently visited Europe several times.

INDEX